AS Chemistry
UNIT 2

AQA

Module 2: Foundation Physical and Inorganic Chemistry

Neil Goldie

Philip Allan Updates
Market Place
Deddington
Oxfordshire
OX15 0SE

tel: 01869 338652
fax: 01869 337590
e-mail: sales@philipallan.co.uk
www.philipallan.co.uk

ISBN-13: 978-0-86003-726-2
ISBN-10: 0-86003-726-6

This Guide has been written specifically to support students preparing for the AQA AS Chemistry Unit 2 examination. The content has been neither approved nor endorsed by AQA and remains the sole responsibility of the author.

Printed by Raithby, Lawrence & Co. Ltd, Leicester

P00500

Contents

Introduction

■ ■ ■

Content Guidance

■ ■ ■

Questions and Answers

Introduction

About this guide

This guide is for students following the AQA Chemistry AS specification. It deals with Unit 2, which examines the content of **Module 2: Foundation Physical and Inorganic Chemistry**. This unit covers 30% of the total AS marks or 15% of the total A-level marks. The $1\frac{1}{2}$ hour exam consists of several structured questions, of varying length, which are all compulsory. Some questions require short answers while some are more extended, needing answers written in continuous prose. There are 90 marks available on this paper.

Questions in Unit 2 assume knowledge and understanding of the concepts of Module 1. In addition, there are many numerous principles and concepts covered in Module 2 that must be understood so that you can answer questions set in an unfamiliar situation.

The key to success

It is essential that you can recall the basic facts and definitions, but a deeper understanding of the subject is essential if you want to achieve the top grades. The key to success in chemistry is *to understand the fundamental concepts* and *be able to apply them to new and unfamiliar situations*. Good examination technique is also an important factor, enabling you to work more effectively in the exam and gain access to the marks needed for a top grade.

This guide allows you to look again at the content of the specification, to test yourself at the end of each section and to assess your own work. It is essential that you read through the examiner's comments because they will help you improve your exam technique. Once you have completely worked through this guide, you will be very aware of your weak areas and it is these areas that you really need to address. Make a list of these weak areas and discuss any problems with other students in your class and with your teacher.

Using the guide

This guide has three sections:
- **Introduction** — this provides guidance on study and revision, together with advice on approaches and techniques to ensure you answer the examination questions in the best way that you can.
- **Content Guidance** — this section is not intended to be a textbook. It offers guidelines on the main features of the content of Unit 2, together with particular advice on making study more productive.

- **Questions and Answers** — this shows you the sort of questions you can expect in the unit test. Grade-A answers are provided; these are followed by examiner's comments. Careful consideration of these will improve your answers and, much more importantly, will improve your understanding of the chemistry involved.

Revise a topic using the Content Guidance section as a guide. If there is something you do not understand, you should also refer to your own class notes and textbooks.

It is essential that you write down *specific* questions and discuss them with your teacher. For instance, 'Please could you explain redox again' is not a good use of your time if you understand most of the features of reduction, oxidation and oxidation states. 'Please could you explain how to deduce half-equations and how they combine to produce an overall redox equation' is more specific and shows that you have worked hard to identify weak areas.

Once you have revised a particular topic thoroughly, you should attempt the relevant questions, in the Question and Answer section, *without* looking at the grade-A answer.

Compare your answer with the grade-A answer and estimate your own performance. A rough guide to use is 80% = grade A, 70% = grade B, 60% = grade C, etc. However, these grade boundaries are adjusted, depending on the performance of the candidates.

Read through the examiner's comments to find out if you have made any of the common mistakes and to see how you could improve your technique. The comments also give some alternative answers.

Make a note of *specific questions* that caused you problems and discuss them with other students and your teacher.

Revision schedule

- Plan your revision schedule carefully.
- It is essential that you revise regularly.
- Leave yourself enough time to cover all the material. You need to go through each topic once as a basic minimum and then go through the weak areas again.
- In the weeks leading up to the exam, it is the weak areas that you should be revising, not every topic.
- In each revision session do not try to achieve too much. Revise one topic per session, e.g. bond enthalpies. Here is one way to structure your session:
  - revise from the Content Guidance section (and your own notes)
  - make a brief written summary (no more than an A4 sheet of paper)
  - attempt the questions
  - mark your answer
  - read the examiner's comments

- If you have scored a grade A, then tick the relevant section of the topic in the table shown below. You must have a break before you start the revision of the next topic.
- If there are weak areas and questions that you clearly do not understand, then write down specific questions ready for discussion with your teacher.
- Finally, make sure that you attempt all the past paper questions from the exam board and study the mark schemes carefully. Questions may be repeated or similar questions set.

Revision checklist

Once you have completed your revision and you feel that you completely understand the topic fully, tick the relevant box. If you have identified a weak area, place a cross in the relevant box.

Energetics

Topics	Details	✓ or ✗
Enthalpy change	Exothermic and endothermic reactions	
	Standard conditions	
	Enthalpy of formation and enthalpy of combustion	
Calorimetry	Use $q = mc\Delta T$ to deduce the enthalpy changes for combustion and neutralisation reactions	
Hess's law	Define Hess's law	
	Calculations on Hess's law	
Bond enthalpies	Principle of mean bond enthalpies	
	Calculations involving mean bond enthalpies	

Kinetics

Topics	Details	✓ or ✗
Collision theory	Understand the essential conditions for a reaction to take place	
Maxwell–Boltzmann distribution	Draw the distribution of molecular energies at different temperatures	
Factors affecting the rate of a reaction	Concentration, surface area, temperature and catalysts	
Catalysis	Define energy of activation	
	Define catalyst	
	General role of a catalyst	
Practical situations	Use the principles of kinetics to explain graphs produced from experiments	

Equilibria

Topics	Details	✓ or X
The dynamic nature of equilibria	Reversible nature of reactions	
	The essential features of an equilibrium	
Le Chatelier's principle	Use of this principle to predict the effect of pressure, temperature and concentration on the equilibrium position	
Industrial processes	Apply the principles of equilibria, kinetics and economics to industrial processes and understand the need for compromise conditions	

Redox reactions

Topics	Details	✓ or X
Oxidation and reduction	Define in terms of electron loss and electron gain	
Oxidation states	Recall the rules for working out oxidation states	
	Work out the oxidation state for an element in a compound or ion	
Redox equations	Construct half-equations	
	Combine half-equations to produce an overall redox equation	

Halogens

Topics	Details	✓ or X
Trends in physical properties	The trend in electronegativity	
	The trend in boiling points	
Trends in chemical properties	The oxidising power of the halogens	
	The halogen displacement reactions	
Trends in the properties of the halides	The reducing power of the halides	
	The reaction of the halides with concentrated sulphuric acid	
	Distinguishing between halides using silver nitrate	
Uses of chlorine and the estimation of chlorate(I)	Reaction of chlorine with water	
	Reaction of chlorine with NaOH	
	The equations for the reaction of NaClO with KI and the reaction of I_2 with $Na_2S_2O_3$	
	The estimation of the amount of NaClO in bleach	

Extraction of metals

Topics	Details	✓ or ✗
Reduction of metal oxides with carbon	The extraction of iron	
	The conversion to steel	
	Pollution problems	
	Limitations of carbon reduction	
Reduction of metal oxides by electrolysis	The extraction of aluminium	
The reduction of metal halides with metal	The extraction of titanium	
	The reason why the extraction process is so expensive	
Economic factors and recycling	The recycling of iron and aluminium	
	The benefits and problems associated with recycling	

Unit Test 2

If you have revised thoroughly, completed all the questions in this guide and discussed problems with other students and your teacher, you should enjoy the exam. If you have completed all the AQA past papers, then the style of the paper will be very familiar and you will recognise some questions in the exam because they will be similar to previous questions.

Do not begin to write as soon as you open the paper — quickly scan the questions first.

It is *not* essential that you answer the questions in order. If the first question is difficult, then leave it to the end. It *is* essential that you answer *all* the questions.

You will have enough time to answer all the questions provided that you keep your answers concise and you do not include irrelevant information. It is easy to waste time writing out a section of your notes that is totally irrelevant to the question asked. Do not repeat the question when starting your answer. The key to exam success is achieving the maximum number of marks in the minimum number of words.

The mark allocation at the end of each question should be used to estimate the amount of detail needed in your answer. If there is 1 mark available, the examiner will be looking for a key word or phrase and certainly no more than one sentence. If there are 4 marks available, you should include four key points, which usually means writing four short sentences.

No marks are available for producing neat answers, but it certainly helps the examiners when they are marking your work. Untidy diagrams may become inaccurate and this definitely loses marks.

Terms used in examination questions

Give/state/name
These appear in many of the early structured questions. You need only write one or two words. There is usually 1 mark available for questions of this type.

Define
It is essential that you learn all your definitions. You need to state a definition or law very concisely. Definitions are usually worth 2 or 3 marks and the mark allocation indicates how many key points must be included.

Complete
You have to finish off a diagram, a graph or a table.

Draw/show by means of a diagram
Most drawings require only a simple sketch. It must be clear and accurate, but the examiner does not expect it to be of the same standard as that seen in your textbook. Poor presentation can make diagrams inaccurate and this is when marks are lost.

Calculate or determine
Use information to calculate a final answer that must be shown to the correct number of significant figures. Always show your working and include appropriate units after the final answer.

Write a balanced equation
In chemical equations, state symbols are not usually expected unless the examiner specifically asks for them. In physical processes and thermochemistry equations, state symbols are usually expected. For example, the combustion of methane is:

$$CH_4(g) + 2O_2(g) \longrightarrow CO_2(g) + 2H_2O(l)$$

Describe/explain
'Describe' means only give a description, whereas 'explain' requires a reason or interpretation. Both these terms mean more depth is required in your answer. You can judge how much detail is required by the mark allocation. 10 marks means that ten key points must be covered and this will probably require you to write a minimum of ten sentences. In general, most candidates write too much and give far too much detail.

Use
Questions using this term often include some data. Make sure you do use the data and include them in your answer. You may have to use a basic principle and apply it to a new and unfamiliar situation.

Suggest
This means that you will probably have not come across the material in the question before. You will have been taught the basic principle and now you have to apply this knowledge to an unfamiliar situation.

Content
Guidance

This section covers the content of **Module 2: Foundation Physical and Inorganic Chemistry**. This module builds on your knowledge and understanding of Module 1. Module 2 appears to have less factual content than Module 1, particularly in the physical chemistry topics. In order to achieve a top grade, it is essential that you fully understand the basic concepts and that you can apply them to unfamiliar situations. The content of this module falls into six sections, which are summarised below.

Energetics

Recall several definitions: standard enthalpy of combustion, standard enthalpy of formation and Hess's law. Understand the basic principles of Hess's law, mean bond enthalpies and calorimetry and carry out calculations on these topics.

Kinetics

Understand the collision theory and interpret diagrams on the distribution of molecular energies. State and explain the effect of concentration, surface area, temperature and catalysts on the rate of a reaction. Explain these factors using the diagrams that show the distribution of molecular energies.

Equilibria

Understand the basic concept of equilibria. Use Le Chatelier's principle to predict the effects of changes in temperature, pressure and concentration on the position of equilibrium. Understand the effect of a catalyst on a reaction at equilibrium. Apply the basic principles of equilibria, rate and economics to industrial processes and understand the need for compromise conditions.

Redox reactions

Define redox in terms of electron transfer. Deduce the oxidation state of any element in a compound or ion. Write half-equations for reduction and oxidation and combine these half-equations to produce an overall redox equation.

Group 7: the halogens

State and explain the trends in the physical and chemical properties of the halogens. State and explain the trends in the properties of the halide ions. Recall the reactions of chlorine with water and sodium hydroxide. Carry out calculations to estimate the amount of sodium chlorate(I) in bleach. This section relies on your understanding of the basic principles of redox.

Extraction of metals

Understand the methods employed in the extraction of iron, aluminium and titanium. Recall the specific details of each extraction process. Understand the issues related to the recycling of iron and aluminium and the pollution problems associated with the extraction of metals.

Energetics

You need to be able to recall definitions both in words and by the use of equations. The definitions of exothermic and endothermic reactions, standard enthalpy change, the enthalpy of combustion, the enthalpy of formation and Hess's law are required. These definitions must be very precise and the equations should include state symbols where appropriate. You need to be able to perform calculations using Hess's law, mean bond enthalpies and calorimetry.

Definitions

Exothermic reactions

- The system gives out energy to the surroundings and causes an *increase in temperature*.
- The sign of ΔH is *negative*.
- The reaction can be represented on an energy diagram where the *arrow goes down* from reactants to products.

Example: the formation of ammonia

$$N_2 + 3H_2 \longrightarrow 2NH_3 \quad \Delta H = -92 \text{ kJ mol}^{-1}$$

N$_2$ + 3H$_2$

$\Delta H = -92$ kJ mol^{-1}

2NH$_3$

Endothermic reactions

- The system takes in energy from the surroundings and causes a *decrease in temperature*.
- The sign of ΔH is *positive*.
- The reaction can be represented on an energy diagram where the *arrow goes up* from reactants to products.

Example: dissolving ammonium chloride

$$NH_4Cl(s) \longrightarrow NH_4^+(aq) + Cl^-(aq) \quad \Delta H = +15 \text{ kJ mol}^{-1}$$

NH$_4^+$(aq) + Cl$^-$(aq)

NH$_4$Cl(s) $\quad \Delta H = +15$ kJ mol^{-1}

The standard enthalpy change

The **enthalpy change** is defined as *the heat energy change at constant pressure*. It is indicated by the symbol ΔH where Δ is the 'change in' and H is the heat enthalpy.

The **standard enthalpy change** is represented by $\Delta H^\ominus$.

The symbol $\ominus$ shows that the enthalpy change is measured under standard conditions. These conditions are a pressure of 100 kPa and a specified temperature, usually 298 K.

If a substance exists in more than one **allotropic form**, for example $C_{[graphite]}$ or $C_{[diamond]}$, this must be specified. In calculations, assume graphite unless diamond is specified.

State symbols must be included in the equation when defining an enthalpy change. For example, $H_2O(l)$ refers to water in the liquid state, whereas $H_2O(g)$ refers to water vapour (steam).

Standard enthalpy of combustion

The standard enthalpy of combustion is represented by $\Delta H_c^\ominus$.

This is the enthalpy change when *one mole* of a substance undergoes *complete combustion* in oxygen under **standard conditions** (100 kPa and 298 K), all reactants and products being in their standard states.

Examples
It is important that when you balance an equation, there is only *one mole* of the substance being burnt. You must always include state symbols. All the combustion reactions below are exothermic.

Substance	Equation	Enthalpy change
Hydrogen	$H_2(g) + \frac{1}{2}O_2(g) \longrightarrow H_2O(l)$	-286 kJ mol^{-1}
Methane	$CH_4(g) + 2O_2(g) \longrightarrow CO_2(g) + 2H_2O(l)$	-890 kJ mol^{-1}
Ethanol	$C_2H_5OH(l) + 3O_2(g) \longrightarrow 2CO_2(g) + 3H_2O(l)$	-1371 kJ mol^{-1}

Standard enthalpy of formation

The standard enthalpy of formation is represented by $\Delta H_f^\ominus$.

This is the enthalpy change when *one mole* of a compound is *formed from its elements in their standard states*, at 298 K and 100 kPa.

Examples
Remember, the enthalpy of formation of any element is zero. When balancing an equation, it is essential that only *one mole* of the compound is formed.

Substance	Equation	Enthalpy change
Methane	$C(s) + 2H_2(g) \longrightarrow CH_4(g)$	-75 kJ mol^{-1}
Ethanol	$2C(s) + 3H_2(g) + \frac{1}{2}O_2(g) \longrightarrow C_2H_5OH(l)$	-278 kJ mol^{-1}
Ammonia	$\frac{1}{2}N_2(g) + 1\frac{1}{2}H_2(g) \longrightarrow NH_3(g)$	-46 kJ mol^{-1}

Hess's law

The **enthalpy change** in a chemical reaction is *constant* and *independent of the route taken*, provided that the *states* of the reactants and products are the *same*.

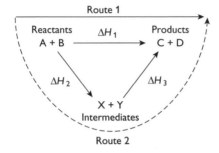

Route 1

Reactants ΔH_1 Products
A + B $\longrightarrow$ C + D

ΔH_2 ΔH_3

X + Y
Intermediates

Route 2

The enthalpy change for route 1 = enthalpy changes of route 2:

$$\Delta H_1 = \Delta H_2 + \Delta H_3$$

The sum of the enthalpy changes for the cyclic process $\Delta H_1 - \Delta H_3 - \Delta H_2 = 0$.

Calculate the unknown enthalpy changes shown below to make sure you understand the general principle of Hess's law. If you alter the direction of the arrow, then you must alter the sign of the enthalpy change.

Example 1

$$A + B \xrightarrow{\Delta H_1 = -50 \text{ kJ mol}^{-1}} C + D$$

ΔH_2 $\Delta H_3 = -100$ kJ mol^{-1}

P + Q

Answer: $\Delta H_2 = +50$ kJ mol^{-1}

Example 2

$$A + B \xrightarrow{\Delta H_1 = +75 \text{ kJ mol}^{-1}} C + D$$

$\Delta H_2 = -50$ kJ mol^{-1} ΔH_3

P + Q

Answer: $\Delta H_3 = -125$ kJ mol^{-1}

Applications of Hess's law

Calculating heats of formation using heats of combustion

- It is essential that you understand the general principle.
- Write the equation for the formation of one mole of the compound from its elements in their standard states.
- Produce a triangle of the three enthalpy changes by listing the mutual oxidation products of the reactants and the products.
- When calculating the enthalpy of formation using Hess's law, remember to change the sign of the enthalpy of combustion of the products.

General principle

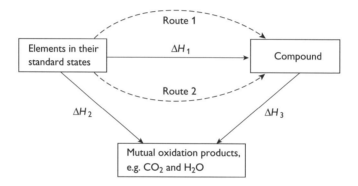

Applying Hess's law:
  enthalpy change of route 1 = enthalpy change of route 2
$$\Delta H_1 = \Delta H_2 - \Delta H_3$$

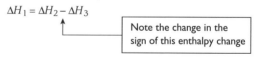

Note the change in the sign of this enthalpy change

Example
Calculate the enthalpy of formation of methane.
- Enthalpy of combustion of carbon = $-393\,kJ\,mol^{-1}$
- Enthalpy of combustion of hydrogen = $-285\,kJ\,mol^{-1}$
- Enthalpy of combustion of methane = $-890\,kJ\,mol^{-1}$

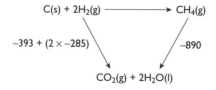

$\Delta H_f = -393 + (2 \times -285) - (-890) = \mathbf{-73\,kJ\,mol^{-1}}$

Calculating enthalpies of reactions using enthalpies of formation

- Write an equation for the conversion of the reactants to the products.
- Produce a triangle by listing the elements in their standard states.
- When calculating the enthalpy of the reaction, using Hess's law, remember to change the sign of the enthalpy of formation of the reactants.

General principle

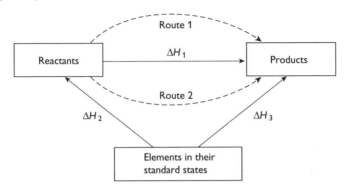

Applying Hess's law:

enthalpy change of route 1 = enthalpy change of route 2

$$\Delta H_1 = -\Delta H_2 + \Delta H_3$$

> Note the change in the sign of this enthalpy change

$$\therefore \Delta H_1 = \Delta H_2 - \Delta H_3$$

ΔH_1 for the reaction = $\Sigma \Delta H_f$ of the products – $\Sigma \Delta H_f$ of the reactants

Example

Calculate the heat change for the reaction of magnesium and carbon dioxide.

- Enthalpy of formation of carbon dioxide is –394 kJ mol^{-1}.
- Enthalpy of formation of magnesium oxide is –602 kJ mol^{-1}.
- Enthalpy of formation of all the elements is zero.

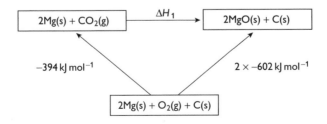

ΔH_1 = $\Sigma \Delta H_f$ of the products – $\Sigma \Delta H_f$ of the reactants

ΔH_1 = (2 × –602) – (–394) = **–810 kJ mol^{-1}**

Bond enthalpies

Calculation of mean bond enthalpies

General principle

When a covalent bond is broken, a certain amount of energy is required. This is called the bond **dissociation enthalpy** or the **bond energy**. The greater the bond energy, the stronger is the bond.

The bond dissociation enthalpy refers to the enthalpy change for the following process, where all the species are in the gaseous state:

$X–Y(g) \longrightarrow X(g) + Y(g)$ ΔH (this ΔH is the bond enthalpy)

In polyatomic molecules (containing more than two atoms), it is more appropriate to quote the mean bond energy:

$Y–X–Y(g) \longrightarrow X(g) + 2Y(g)$ ΔH (the mean bond enthalpy is $\Delta H/2$)

Example

Calculate the mean bond energy of methane.

The energy required to break the first C–H bond in methane is not the same as the second, third or fourth, because they are in different environments.

$CH_4(g) \longrightarrow CH_3(g) + H(g)$ $\Delta H = +426 \, kJ \, mol^{-1}$
$CH_3(g) \longrightarrow CH_2(g) + H(g)$ $\Delta H = +439 \, kJ \, mol^{-1}$
$CH_2(g) \longrightarrow CH(g) + H(g)$ $\Delta H = +451 \, kJ \, mol^{-1}$
$CH(g) \longrightarrow C(g) + H(g)$ $\Delta H = +348 \, kJ \, mol^{-1}$

The mean bond energy can be calculated by measuring the enthalpy change for the breaking of all four bonds, and then dividing this answer by four.

$CH_4(g) \longrightarrow C(g) + 4H(g)$ $\Delta H = +1664 \, kJ \, mol^{-1}$
Mean bond energy $= +1664/4 = +\textbf{416 kJ mol}^{-1}$

Example

Mean bond energies (E) are also calculated by estimating their strength in different compounds. The value of the bond dissociation enthalpy can vary depending upon the environment of the bond.

Compound	CCl_4	CH_3Cl	C_2H_5Cl
$E(C–Cl)/kJ \, mol^{-1}$	+327	+335	+342

The mean bond energy of a carbon–chlorine bond, $E(C–Cl)$, is +338 kJ mol^{-1} when it is averaged over a wide range of compounds (not just these three). When you carry out calculations involving mean bond energies, the final answer is often slightly inaccurate. This is because you are using average values rather than the specific values associated with the bonds broken and formed during a reaction.

Use of mean bond energies in calculations

Mean bond energies can be used to calculate the enthalpy change for simple reactions in the gaseous state. Calculated mean bond energies are not as accurate as experimentally determined heat changes.

General principle

During a chemical reaction, energy is supplied to break bonds (**endothermic**) and energy is released when bonds are formed (**exothermic**).

$\Delta H = \Sigma$(enthalpy of bonds broken) $- \Sigma$(enthalpy of bonds formed)

If the energy released from forming new bonds is greater than the energy needed to break existing bonds, there is a net release of energy and the reaction is exothermic.

If the energy released from forming new bonds is less than the energy needed to break existing bonds, there is a net intake of energy and the reaction is endothermic.

Example

Calculate the heat change for the reaction of methane and oxygen to produce carbon dioxide and steam.

Bond	C–H	O=O	C=O	O–H
Mean bond energy/kJ mol^{-1}	413	498	805	464

$CH_4 + 2(O{=}O) \longrightarrow O{=}C{=}O + 2H_2O$

$\Delta H = 4(C{-}H) + 2(O{=}O) - 2(C{=}O) - 4(O{-}H)$

$\quad = 4(413) + 2(498) - 2(805) - 4(464)$

$\quad = \mathbf{-818\,kJ\,mol^{-1}}$

This is an exothermic reaction.

Calorimetry

Enthalpy change can be determined experimentally in the lab using a calorimeter. This is usually a very simple apparatus, for example a plastic cup surrounded by an expanded polystyrene cup in neutralisation experiments, or aluminium cans in combustion experiments.

The **heat energy**, q, required to change the temperature of a substance can be calculated using the formula shown below.

$q = mc\Delta T$

- q = the heat energy liberated in **kJ**
- m = mass of the substance in **kg**
- ΔT = change in temperature in **K**
- c = the specific heat capacity of the substance

For many chemical reactions in aqueous solution, it can be assumed that the only substance heated is water, which has a specific heat capacity of **4.18 kJ K⁻¹ kg⁻¹**. If the specific heat capacity is quoted as 4.18 J K^{-1} g^{-1} and the mass is entered as grams (g), then the answer for heat energy liberated is in joules (J), which is divided by 1000 to produce an answer in kJ.

Calorimetry experiments

It is essential that you are able to calculate enthalpy changes from data generated by practical work.

Enthalpy of combustion

Accurate enthalpies of combustion are determined experimentally using a bomb calorimeter. In a school laboratory, the enthalpy of combustion is usually determined using simple apparatus such as a spirit burner. However, the values determined are much less exothermic than expected because of heat loss to the surroundings.

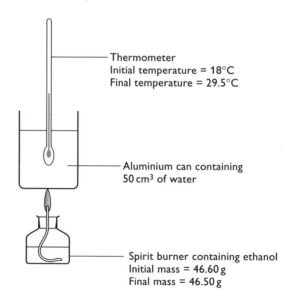

Thermometer
Initial temperature = 18°C
Final temperature = 29.5°C

Aluminium can containing
50 cm³ of water

Spirit burner containing ethanol
Initial mass = 46.60 g
Final mass = 46.50 g

$$C_2H_5OH(l) + 3O_2(g) \longrightarrow 2CO_2(g) + 3H_2O(l)$$

Heat produced: $q = mc\Delta T = 50 \times 10^{-3} \times 4.18 \times 11.5 = 2.4035$ kJ
Moles of ethanol used: $n = m/M_r = 0.1/46 = 2.174 \times 10^{-3}$
Enthalpy of combustion: $\Delta H_c = -q/n = -2.4035/2.174 \times 10^{-3} = $ **–1106 kJ mol⁻¹**

The theoretical value for ethanol is -1371 kJ mol^{-1}.

You are often asked to compare the experimental answer with the theoretical answer. The experimental answer is much less exothermic mainly due to:
- heat loss
- heat taken up by the aluminium calorimeter

- inefficient heat transfer due to lack of stirring
- incomplete combustion of the ethanol

If the experiment were repeated using propan-1-ol, C_3H_7OH, the enthalpy of formation would be more exothermic. This is because propan-1-ol has one more CH_2 group than ethanol. Energy is needed to break the bonds in this CH_2 group — but forming more CO_2 and H_2O liberates more energy.

Enthalpy of neutralisation

The enthalpy of neutralisation is the enthalpy change if one mole of water is formed when an acid neutralises an alkali at 298 K and 100 kPa.

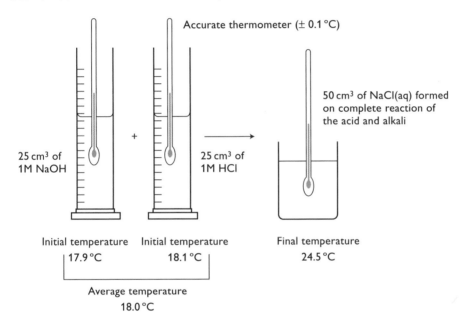

Accurate thermometer ($\pm 0.1\,^\circ$C)

50 cm³ of NaCl(aq) formed on complete reaction of the acid and alkali

25 cm³ of 1M NaOH   +   25 cm³ of 1M HCl

Initial temperature   Initial temperature   Final temperature
17.9 °C   18.1 °C   24.5 °C

Average temperature
18.0 °C

$$NaOH(aq) + HCl(aq) \longrightarrow NaCl(aq) + H_2O(l)$$
$$OH^-(aq) + H^+(aq) \longrightarrow H_2O(l)$$

Temperature change in this reaction = 6.5 °C
Mass of final aqueous solution = 50 g = 50×10^{-3} kg
Heat produced: $q = mc\Delta T = 50 \times 10^{-3} \times 4.18 \times 6.5 = 1.3585$ kJ
Moles of water produced: $n = MV/1000 = 1 \times 25/1000 = 2.5 \times 10^{-2}$
Enthalpy of neutralisation: $\Delta H = -q/n = -1.3585/2.5 \times 10^{-2} = $ **−54 kJ mol⁻¹**

The theoretical answer is -57 kJ mol⁻¹.

The experimental answer is lower than expected due to heat loss to the surroundings. Similar experiments with other strong acids and alkalis will also liberate -57 kJ mol⁻¹. This is because all strong acids and alkalis fully dissociate, so the ionic equation for all these reactions is $OH^-(aq) + H^+(aq) \longrightarrow H_2O(l)$.

Kinetics

You need to be able to explain the rate of a chemical reaction using collision theory and to describe the Maxwell–Boltzmann distribution of molecular energies. You should be able to explain qualitatively how concentration, surface area, temperature and catalysts alter the rate of a chemical reaction.

Collision theory

In order for a chemical reaction to take place, the reactant particles must:
- collide
- possess energy greater than the energy of activation
- collide with the correct orientation

Maxwell–Boltzmann distribution of molecular energies

In a given sample of a gas, the molecules possess varying amounts of energy. This can be represented by the following distribution curve.

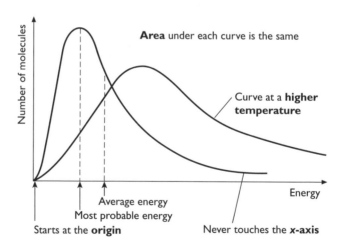

- The curve for the higher temperature is broader than the curve for the lower temperature.
- The curve for the higher temperature has a lower peak and is displaced to the right of the curve with the lower temperature.
- Both curves start at the origin because no particles have zero energy.

- The area under both curves is the same, because this represents the total number of molecules in the system, which thus remains constant.

Factors affecting the rate of a reaction

The rate of a reaction can be defined as the *change in concentration of a substance in unit time*. The units for rate are **mol dm^{-3} s^{-1}**. You have to be able to use collision theory to explain how catalysts and changes in concentration, surface area and temperature alter the rate of a chemical reaction.

Concentration and surface area

When a graph of the concentration of a reagent against time is plotted, *the rate of a reaction* at a particular time is given by the *gradient* of the tangent to the curve at that time.

The initial gradient is the greatest, indicating the initial rate is the fastest. The gradient of the curve falls because the rate of the reaction is decreasing. When the reaction is complete, the gradient falls to zero.

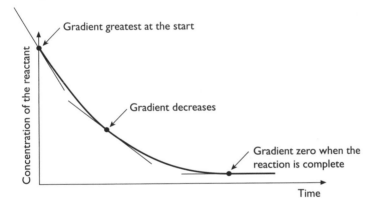

The shape of the graph can be explained by collision theory. As the reaction proceeds, the number of reactant particles decreases. The fewer reactant particles in the system, the lower is the collision frequency — hence the lower the rate of the reaction.

When a solid reactant reacts with a gas or with a substance in solution, breaking the solid into smaller pieces increases the rate of reaction. The smaller pieces have an *increased surface area* available for collision. This leads to an *increased collision frequency*, which leads to an *increased rate of reaction*.

Example

Sketch a graph to show carbon dioxide production against time for the reaction between large lumps of calcium carbonate and 100 cm^3 of 1 M hydrochloric acid. Label the curve A. Sketch a similar graph for a repeat experiment using 50 cm^3 of 2 M hydrochloric acid. Label this curve B. Finally, sketch a graph for an experiment using 50 cm³ of 2 M hydrochloric acid and powdered calcium carbonate. Label this curve C. In all the experiments, calcium carbonate is in excess.

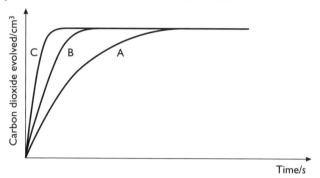

- The amount of carbon dioxide given off depends on the amount of hydrochloric acid used, because the calcium carbonate is in excess.
- In all cases, the number of moles of hydrochloric acid used is the same, so the curves all end at the same point.
- Curve B is initially steeper than curve A, because there is the same number of particles in a smaller volume. This means the initial collision frequency is greater in B than in A.
- Curve C is steeper than curve B, because powdered calcium carbonate offers a greater surface area than large lumps — hence a greater collision frequency.

Temperature

Always use a Maxwell–Boltzmann distribution curve when explaining the effect of temperature. Many collisions are not successful, because the colliding particles do not possess the **energy of activation**. This is defined as the minimum energy that reactant particles must possess for a reaction to occur.

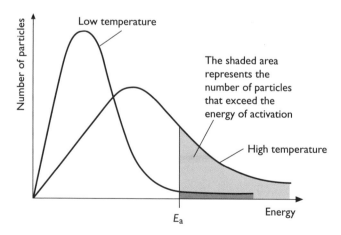

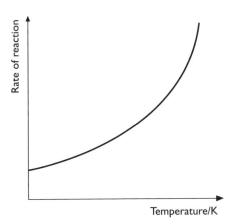

An increase in temperature leads to a dramatic increase in the rate of chemical reactions. Increasing the temperature increases the average kinetic energy of the particles, so they move faster and the collision frequency increases. However, the dramatic increase is due to the significant increase in the number of particles with energy greater than the energy of activation, so there are now many more successful collisions.

Catalysts

You have to be able to define the term catalyst and explain how catalysts work in terms of lowering the energy of activation.

A catalyst is a substance that *alters the rate of a chemical reaction, without being itself used up* during the reaction.

A catalyst works by *providing an alternative route*, which has a *lower energy of activation*. This is illustrated on the energy profile diagram below.

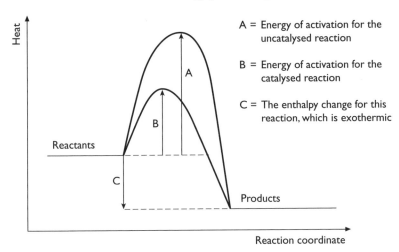

A = Energy of activation for the uncatalysed reaction

B = Energy of activation for the catalysed reaction

C = The enthalpy change for this reaction, which is exothermic

A lower energy of activation means that more particles have energy greater than the energy of activation, so there are more successful collisions.

Always use the Maxwell–Boltzmann distribution curve when explaining the effect of a catalyst, as below.

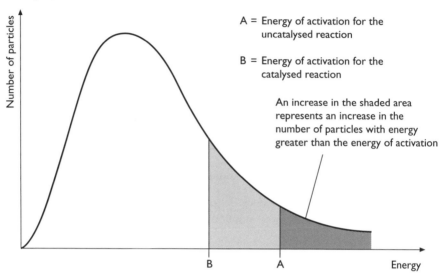

A = Energy of activation for the uncatalysed reaction

B = Energy of activation for the catalysed reaction

An increase in the shaded area represents an increase in the number of particles with energy greater than the energy of activation

Examples of industrial catalysts

You may be asked to give an example of an industrial catalyst and the process that it catalyses. Iron in the Haber process ($N_2 + 3H_2 \rightleftharpoons 2NH_3$) and vanadium(V) oxide in the Contact process ($2SO_2 + O_2 \rightleftharpoons 2SO_3$) are good examples.

Equilibria

You need to understand the difference between complete and reversible reactions and be able to describe the dynamic nature of equilibria. You will not be expected to define Le Chatelier's principle but you must be able to apply it, so that you can predict the effect on the position of equilibrium of changing the concentration, temperature or pressure. You will then be able to discuss the choice of compromise conditions for industrial processes, in terms of yield, rate and costs.

Complete reactions continue until one of the reactants is used up and the reaction stops, i.e. the reaction goes to completion. For example, the reaction of magnesium and oxygen, which is represented by the following equation:

$$2Mg + O_2 \longrightarrow 2MgO$$

Reversible reactions do not go to completion. For example, nitrogen and hydrogen combine in the presence of an iron catalyst to produce ammonia. The ammonia can decompose to produce nitrogen and hydrogen. The overall reaction is represented by the equation below.

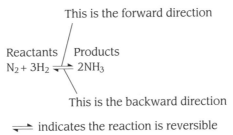

$\rightleftharpoons$ indicates the reaction is reversible

The dynamic nature of equilibria

In a reversible reaction, a chemical equilibrium is established when the rate of the forward reaction is equal to the rate of the backward (or reverse) reaction. A dynamic equilibrium is achieved when:

- the reversible reaction takes place in a closed system
- the reaction is continuous and still proceeding
- the rate of the forward reaction equals the rate of the backward reaction
- the concentration of the reactants and products remains constant

The concentrations of reactants and products remain constant at equilibrium under given conditions of temperature and pressure.

Changing the conditions of a reaction at equilibrium

The qualitative effect of changing the reaction conditions can be predicted by using **Le Chatelier's principle**: *a system at equilibrium will react to oppose any change imposed upon it.*

The effect of a change in concentration

Basic principle

$$A + B \rightleftharpoons C + D$$

- If the concentration of reactant A or B is increased, then the position of the equilibrium is displaced to the right and more product is obtained.
- If product C or D is removed, the position of the equilibrium is also displaced to the right to replace the product.
- If product C or D is added, the equilibrium position shifts to the left to remove the product.

Example 1: esterification

In esterification an organic acid reacts with an alcohol to produce an ester and water.

$$CH_3COOH + C_2H_5OH \rightleftharpoons CH_3COOC_2H_5 + H_2O$$

- If more ethanol (C_2H_5OH) is added to the reaction mixture, the equilibrium position is displaced to the right.
- If more water is added to the reaction mixture, the equilibrium position is displaced to the left.
- If concentrated sulphuric acid is added, it removes the water. In this case, the equilibrium position shifts to the right.

Example 2: the Haber process

In the Haber process, the reactants and products are gaseous. The concentration of the gases is expressed in terms of partial pressures.

$$N_2 + 3H_2 \rightleftharpoons 2NH_3$$

- If the partial pressure of nitrogen is increased, the equilibrium position is displaced to the right and more ammonia is produced.
- If the partial pressure of ammonia is decreased (by removing the ammonia as it forms), the equilibrium position is displaced to the right and more ammonia is produced.

The effect of a change in total pressure

Basic principle

$$3A(g) + B(g) \rightleftharpoons 2C(g)$$

- Changes in total pressure have a significant effect only in equilibrium reactions involving gases.
- An increase in total pressure displaces the equilibrium in the direction of fewer moles of gas.
- The system responds, trying to reduce the pressure by reducing the number of moles of gas present.
- In the case shown above, an increase in pressure causes the equilibrium position to shift to the right, because there are four gaseous particles on the left of the equation and only two on the right.

Example 1: steam reforming of methane

$$CH_4(g) + H_2O(g) \rightleftharpoons 3H_2(g) + CO(g)$$

- The number of gaseous reactants is two and the number of gaseous products is four.
- Moving in the forward direction leads to an increase in pressure, because the number of moles increases from two to four.
- Reducing the total pressure on the system increases the yield of carbon monoxide: the system responds by trying to increase the pressure and the equilibrium position moves to the right.

Example 2: the Haber process

$$N_2(g) + 3H_2(g) \rightleftharpoons 2NH_3(g)$$

- The number of gaseous reactants is four and the number of gaseous products is two.
- Moving in the forward direction leads to a decrease in pressure, because the number of moles decreases from four to two.
- Increasing the total pressure on the system increases the yield of ammonia: the system responds by trying to decrease the pressure and the equilibrium position moves to the right.

The effect of a change in temperature

Basic principle

$$A(g) + B(g) \rightleftharpoons 2C(g) \qquad \Delta H = -x\,kJ\,mol^{-1}$$

Negative means exothermic

- If the temperature is increased, the position of the equilibrium shifts to oppose the change and it moves in the direction that would lower the temperature.
- In the case shown above, the reaction is exothermic in the forward direction, so an increase in temperature shifts the equilibrium position to the left and there are fewer products in the equilibrium mixture.
- If the reaction were endothermic in the forward direction, the enthalpy change would be positive. An increase in temperature would shift the position of the equilibrium to the right and there would be more products in the equilibrium mixture.

Example 1: decomposition of dinitrogen tetraoxide

$$N_2O_4 \rightleftharpoons 2NO_2 \qquad \Delta H = +58\,kJ$$

- The reaction is endothermic in the forward direction.
- If the temperature is increased, the equilibrium responds to try to reduce the effect.
- The equilibrium position shifts to the right (in the endothermic direction) and more NO_2 is produced.

Example 2: the Contact process

$$2SO_2 + O_2 \rightleftharpoons 2SO_3 \qquad \Delta H = -196\,kJ$$

- The reaction is exothermic in the forward direction.
- If the temperature is increased, the equilibrium responds to try to reduce the effect.
- The equilibrium position shifts to the left (in the endothermic direction) and less SO_3 is produced.

The effect of catalysts on the equilibrium position

- The addition of a catalyst to a mixture at equilibrium has no effect on the composition of the equilibrium mixture.

- Catalysts speed up the rate of the forward and backward reactions equally.
- There is no effect on the equilibrium *position* but the *rate* of attainment of equilibrium is increased.

The importance of equilibria in industrial processes

You need to be able to apply the basic principles of equilibria, kinetics and economics to industrial processes. The aim of any industrial process is to convert reactants to products:

- quickly (high rate)
- completely (high yield)
- cheaply (low fuel costs)

The synthesis of ammonia by the Haber process is used as an example.

$$N_2(g) + 3H_2(g) \rightleftharpoons 2NH_3(g) \qquad \Delta H = -92 \text{ kJ mol}^{-1}$$

Condition	Equilibria	Kinetics	Cost
Pressure	High pressure favours a high yield because the number of moles decreases in the forward direction and the equilibrium position shifts to the right	High pressure favours a high rate, because there are more particles per unit volume, leading to an increased collision frequency and therefore more successful collisions	High pressures are very expensive; the costs of building and maintaining the plant are higher, as are fuel costs
Temperature	The reaction is exothermic; a low temperature produces a high yield, because the equilibrium position shifts to the right to try to increase the temperature	High temperatures favour a high rate, because particles have more energy resulting in a higher collision frequency; there are more successful collisions because more particles have energy greater than the activation energy	High temperatures result in increased fuel costs
Catalyst	Adding a catalyst does not alter the equilibrium position, because the rates of the forward and backward reactions are increased equally	A catalyst lowers the energy of activation; more particles will have energy greater than the activation energy, so there will be many more successful collisions	Use of a catalyst lowers fuel costs; however, it eventually becomes poisoned and so has to be replaced on a regular basis

The actual conditions employed are usually compromise conditions. In the case of the Haber process, these are:
- pressure, 2×10^4 kPa
- temperature, 650–720 K
- catalyst, iron

You may be asked to discuss the reasons for compromise conditions. In any discussion, base your answer on the table above. Construct three separate paragraphs covering pressure, temperature and the use of a catalyst. In each paragraph, refer briefly to equilibria, kinetics and cost.

Redox reactions

Oxidation states

No formal definition of the term oxidation state is required. However, you must understand the basic principle in order to work out the oxidation state of an element in any compound or ion.

Basic principle

The oxidation state is:
- the charge on an atom in a compound or ion
- independent of the nature of bonding in the compound, which is always regarded as totally ionic

Example 1: potassium chloride (ionic)

The oxidation states in ionic compounds are easy to predict because they are equivalent to the charges on the ions.

KCl

K is +1   Cl is –1

Example 2: water (covalent)

Water is a covalent molecule. However, if you assume it is ionic, then each hydrogen would have a charge of +1 and the oxygen would have a charge of –2 and so the overall charge for water is zero.

O is –2

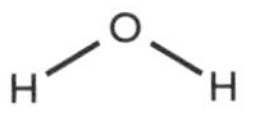

H   O   H

Each H is +1

To decide which atom has a negative oxidation state and which has a positive oxidation state, you need to know the trend in electronegativities:
- the more electronegative atom has a negative oxidation state
- the less electronegative atom has a positive oxidation state

Basic rules for oxidation states

It is essential that you learn the basic rules, which are tabulated below. If you know the rules, you will be able to deduce the oxidation state of any element in a compound or ion.

Rules	Examples
The oxidation state of an atom in a pure element is zero	$Fe = 0$, $Cl_2 = 0$, $Na = 0$, $H_2 = 0$
The sum of all the oxidation states of the atoms in a compound is zero	$NaCl = 0$, $H_2O = 0$, $CO_2 = 0$, $CuSO_4 = 0$
Some metal elements have fixed oxidation states in compounds: • group 1 metals are +1 in compounds • group 2 metals are +2 in compounds • group 3 metals are +3 in compounds	Li^+, Na^+, K^+ Mg^{2+}, Ca^{2+} Al^{3+}
Hydrogen is +1 in compounds (except in metal hydrides)	H_2O; $H = +1$, $O = -2$
Hydrogen is −1 in metal hydrides	NaH; $Na = +1$, $H = -1$
Fluorine is the most electronegative element in the periodic table and it is always −1	CaF_2; $Ca = +2$, $F = -1$
Halogens are also −1, except where the other element is more electronegative	LiI; $Li = +1$, $I = -1$ ICl; $I = +1$, $Cl = -1$
Oxygen is always −2 (except in peroxides, where it is −1)	CO_2; $C = +4$, $O = -2$ H_2O_2; $H = +1$, $O = -1$
The oxidation state of an element in an atomic ion equals the charge on the ion	$Fe^{2+} = +2$, $Cl^- = -1$
The sum of the oxidation numbers of the atoms making up a molecular ion equals the charge on the molecular ion	MnO_4^-; $Mn = +7$, $O = -2 \times 4 = -8$; $+7 - 8 = -1$
Many elements have variable oxidation states, for example manganese	MnO_4^-; $Mn = +7$ MnO_4^{2-}; $Mn = +6$ MnO_2; $Mn = +4$ $MnCl_2$; $Mn = +2$

Exercise on oxidation states

The only way that you can test your understanding of the basic rules is to work out some oxidation states. Cover up the right-hand column of the table below and then deduce the oxidation state of the *named* element in the compounds or ions listed.

Question	Element	Oxidation state
(1)	Sodium in NaI	+1
(2)	Hydrogen in H_2S	+1
(3)	Chlorine in PCl_5	−1
(4)	Sulphur in SF_6	+6
(5)	Iron in Fe_2O_3	+3
(6)	Nitrogen in NH_3	−3
(7)	Nitrogen in N_2H_4	−2
(8)	Titanium in $TiCl_3$	+3
(9)	Chlorine in NaClO	+1
(10)	Sulphur in SO_2	+4
(11)	Sulphur in SO_3	+6
(12)	Sulphur in SO_3^{2-}	+4
(13)	Sulphur in SO_4^{2-}	+6
(14)	Nitrogen in NO_2^-	+3
(15)	Nitrogen in NO_3^-	+5
(16)	Nitrogen in NO_2	+4
(17)	Nitrogen in N_2O_4	+4
(18)	Chromium in K_2CrO_4	+6
(19)	Chromium in $Cr_2O_7^{2-}$	+6
(20)	Vanadium in V_2O_5	+5

Recognising redox reactions

You need to be able to recognise redox reactions. If a reaction involves either electron transfer or changes in oxidation state, it is a redox reaction.

Basic principles

- Redox is defined in terms of electron transfer.
- **Oxidation is the loss of electrons** and **reduction is the gain of electrons** (OILRIG — **o**xidation **i**s **l**oss, **r**eduction **i**s **g**ain).
- In a redox reaction, electrons pass from the reducing agent to the oxidising agent.
- A **reducing agent** is an **electron donor**.
- An **oxidising agent** is an **electron acceptor**.
- Redox reactions can be recognised by changes in the oxidation state of the species.
- Electron loss brings about an **increase in oxidation state** — this is **oxidation**.
- Electron gain brings about a **decrease in oxidation state** — this is **reduction**.

Example 1: reaction of copper(II) oxide with ammonia

$$3CuO(s) + 3NH_3(g) \longrightarrow 3Cu(s) + N_2(g) + 3H_2O(l)$$

+2   −3   0   0

- The oxidation state of copper has decreased from +2 to 0, so it has gained electrons and has been reduced.
- The oxidation state of nitrogen has increased from −3 to 0, so it has lost electrons and has been oxidised.
- Copper(II) oxide is the oxidising agent in this reaction and ammonia is the reducing agent.

Example 2: reaction of hydrogen bromide with concentrated sulphuric acid

$$H_2SO_4 + 3HBr \longrightarrow Br_2 + SO_2 + 2H_2O$$

+6   −1   0   +4

- The oxidation state of sulphur has decreased from +6 to +4, so it has gained electrons and has been reduced.
- The oxidation state of bromine has increased from −1 to 0, so it has lost electrons and has been oxidised.
- Sulphuric acid is the oxidising agent in this reaction and hydrogen bromide is the reducing agent.

Half-equations for redox reactions

You need to be able to write half-equations to describe reduction and oxidation processes. The reactants and the products will be given.

Basic principle

There is a clear method to follow in producing any half-equation, provided that the reagents and the products are known:

- Write down the reagents and products, which should have been given in the question.
- Balance the oxygen atoms with **water** molecules.
- Balance the hydrogen atoms with **hydrogen ions** (H^+).
- Balance the charges with **electrons**.
- Check the equation, using the changes in the oxidation states.

Example 1

Potassium sulphate(IV) contains the SO_3^{2-} ion. This can act as a reducing agent in acidic solution and is itself oxidised to SO_4^{2-}.

- $SO_3^{2-} \longrightarrow SO_4^{2-}$
- $SO_3^{2-} + H_2O \longrightarrow SO_4^{2-}$
- $SO_3^{2-} + H_2O \longrightarrow SO_4^{2-} + 2H^+$
- $SO_3^{2-} + H_2O \longrightarrow SO_4^{2-} + 2H^+ + 2e-$
- Check: S(+4) $\longrightarrow$ S(+6) loses 2 electrons

Example 2

Potassium manganate(VII) contains the MnO_4^- ion. This can act as an oxidising agent in acidic solution and is itself reduced to Mn^{2+}.

- $MnO_4^- \longrightarrow Mn^{2+}$
- $MnO_4^- \longrightarrow Mn^{2+} + 4H_2O$
- $MnO_4^- + 8H^+ \longrightarrow Mn^{2+} + 4H_2O$
- $MnO_4^- + 8H^+ + 5e^- \longrightarrow Mn^{2+} + 4H_2O$
- Check: $Mn(+7) \longrightarrow Mn(+2)$ requires 5 electrons

Example 3

Sulphuric acid contains the SO_4^{2-} ion. This can act as an oxidising agent in acidic solution and is itself reduced to H_2S.

- $SO_4^{2-} \longrightarrow H_2S$
- $SO_4^{2-} \longrightarrow H_2S + 4H_2O$
- $SO_4^{2-} + 10H^+ \longrightarrow H_2S + 4H_2O$
- $SO_4^{2-} + 10H^+ + 8e^- \longrightarrow H_2S + 4H_2O$
- Check: $S(+6) \longrightarrow S(-2)$ requires 8 electrons

Combining half-equations to make redox equations

You will meet this type of question in the sections on halogens, particularly halogen displacement reactions and the reactions of sodium halides with concentrated sulphuric acid.

Basic principle

- Before adding together two half-equations, make sure that the numbers of electrons in the half-equations are the same.
- Electrons cancel out when you add the two half-equations together.
- Electrons never appear in the final redox equation.

Example 1: the reaction of potassium bromide with chlorine

1st half-equation: $2Br^- \longrightarrow Br_2 + 2e^-$
2nd half-equation: $Cl_2 + 2e^- \longrightarrow 2Cl^-$
Adding together: $2Br^- + Cl_2 \longrightarrow Br_2 + 2Cl^-$

Example 2: oxidation of bromide ions by sulphuric acid to give bromine and sulphur dioxide

1st half-equation: $2Br^- \longrightarrow Br_2 + 2e^-$
2nd half-equation: $H_2SO_4 + 2H^+ + 2e^- \longrightarrow SO_2 + 2H_2O$
Adding together: $H_2SO_4 + 2H^+ + 2Br^- \longrightarrow SO_2 + 2H_2O + Br_2$

Example 3: oxidation of iodide ions by sulphuric acid to give iodine and hydrogen sulphide

1st half-equation: $2I^- \longrightarrow I_2 + 2e^-$

2nd half-equation: $H_2SO_4 + 8H^+ + 8e^- \longrightarrow H_2S + 4H_2O$

Before adding together, the *first half-equation must be multiplied by 4*, so that 8 electrons are being lost in the oxidation process.

1st half equation: $8I^- \longrightarrow 4I_2 + 8e^-$

Adding together: $H_2SO_4 + 8H^+ + 8I^- \longrightarrow H_2S + 4H_2O + 4I_2$

Group 7: the halogens

Most questions in this section concentrate on chlorine, bromine and iodine. However, if you understand the trends in physical and chemical properties in the halogen group, you should be able to predict the properties of fluorine and astatine.

It is assumed that you understand the basic principles covered in Module 1. Questions could be asked on the electron configuration of halogen atoms, the bonding found between atoms in halogen molecules and the forces between halogen molecules.
- Group 7 elements have *7 electrons* in the outer shell. (Chlorine = $1s^2 2s^2 2p^6\, \mathbf{3s^2\, 3p^5}$)
- The elements exist as **covalent diatomic molecules** in which the atoms are held together by *strong* **covalent bonds**.
- The halogen molecules are held together by *weak* **van der Waals forces**.

Trends in physical properties

Electronegativity

You need to be able to define and explain, in terms of atomic structure, the electronegativity trend in halogen atoms.

Electronegativity is the ability of an atom to withdraw electron density (or an electron pair) from a covalent bond. It *decreases down the group* due to:
- an increase in the number of shells
- an increase in atomic radius
- an increase in the amount of shielding
- a decrease in attraction for the electron density in a covalent bond

Boiling point

You need to be able to describe the trend in the boiling points of the halogens and to explain this trend in terms of the relative strength of the intermolecular forces.

Fluorine is a gas, chlorine is a gas, bromine is a liquid and iodine is a solid.

Boiling points increase down the group due to:
- an increase in the size of the molecules
- an increase in the number of electrons
- more chance of an instantaneous dipole
- greater van der Waals forces between the molecules

Trends in chemical properties

This section concentrates on the oxidising ability of the halogens. You need to understand the concept of redox, to be able to define an oxidising agent in terms of electrons, explain the trend in oxidising power in terms of atomic structure and illustrate the relative oxidising power of the halogens, using displacement reactions.

An oxidising agent is an electron acceptor. Halogens readily accept electrons, but the ability to attract an electron decreases going down the group.

Oxidising power decreases down the group due to:
- an increase in the number of electron shells
- an increase in atomic radius
- an increase in the amount of shielding
- a decrease in the ability to attract an electron

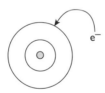

The order of oxidising power is $F_2 > Cl_2 > Br_2 > I_2$. This is shown in **displacement reactions** — a more reactive halogen always displaces a less reactive halogen from its salt solution.

When chlorine is added to an aqueous solution of potassium bromide, a *yellow solution* is formed due to the presence of bromine.

$$Cl_2 + 2Br^- \longrightarrow 2Cl^- + Br_2$$

When chlorine is added to an aqueous solution of potassium iodide, a *brown colour or black precipitate* forms due to the presence of iodine.

$$Cl_2 + 2I^- \longrightarrow 2Cl^- + I_2$$

When an aqueous bromine solution is added to an aqueous solution of potassium iodide, a *brown colour or black precipitate* forms due to the presence of iodine.

$$Br_2 + 2I^- \longrightarrow 2Br^- + I_2$$

When aqueous solutions of bromine or iodine are added to potassium chloride solution, no reactions take place.

Trends in properties of the halides (I)

This section concentrates on the reducing power of **halide ions**. You need to understand the concept of redox, to be able to define a reducing agent in terms of electrons, to explain the trend in reducing power in terms of atomic structure and to illustrate the relative reducing power of the halide ions using the reaction of the sodium halides with concentrated sulphuric acid.

A reducing agent is an electron donor. Halide ions can donate electrons — this ability increases going down the group.

The reducing power of halide ions increases down the group due to:
- an increase in the number of electron shells
- an increase in **ionic radius**
- an increase in the amount of shielding
- a decrease in the amount of attraction for the outer electron
- an increased ease of electron loss

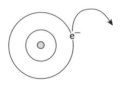

The increase in reducing power is shown by the reaction of sodium halides with concentrated sulphuric acid. The equations for these reactions are given below. Gaseous products are in bold type.

Halide	Equation	Reaction
Chloride	$NaCl + H_2SO_4 \longrightarrow NaHSO_4 + \textbf{HCl}$	Acid–base
Bromide	$NaBr + H_2SO_4 \longrightarrow NaHSO_4 + \textbf{HBr}$	Acid–base
	$2HBr + H_2SO_4 \longrightarrow \textbf{Br}_2 + \textbf{SO}_2 + 2H_2O$	Redox
Iodide	$NaI + H_2SO_4 \longrightarrow NaHSO_4 + \textbf{HI}$	Acid–base
	$2HI + H_2SO_4 \longrightarrow \textbf{I}_2 + \textbf{SO}_2 + 2H_2O$	Redox
	$6HI + H_2SO_4 \longrightarrow 3\textbf{I}_2 + S + 4H_2O$	Redox
	$8HI + H_2SO_4 \longrightarrow 4\textbf{I}_2 + \textbf{H}_2\textbf{S} + 4H_2O$	Redox

The *observations* are summarised as follows:
- All the reactions are exothermic.
- Hydrogen chloride, hydrogen bromide and hydrogen iodide are evolved as misty, white fumes.

- Bromine appears as a brown vapour.
- Iodine appears as a purple vapour or a black solid.
- Sulphur appears as a yellow solid.
- Hydrogen sulphide smells of rotten eggs.

What follows is intended to help you revise the equations and observations above. It covers many of the common questions on the reactions of halide ions with sulphuric acid.

- The first equation for chloride, bromide and iodide is the same. These are **acid–base reactions** or displacement reactions.
- The second equation for bromide and iodide is the same. These are **redox reactions**.
- There are two more equations for iodide. These are also **redox reactions**.

The *concentrated sulphuric acid* acts as a *strong acid* in the acid–base or displacement reactions. It *donates a proton* (H^+) to the halide ion; the halide ion is therefore acting as a base.

The *concentrated sulphuric acid* acts as an *oxidising agent* in the redox reactions. It *accepts electrons* and the oxidation state of the sulphur decreases. The halide ions are donating electrons, so are acting as reducing agents. H_2SO_4 (+6) is reduced to SO_2 (+4), then S (0), then H_2S (–2). (The numbers in brackets are the oxidation states of sulphur.) SO_2, S and H_2S are the reduction products from sulphuric acid.

In order to deduce the number of molecules of hydrogen halide needed in the redox equations, remember:

- if the oxidation state of sulphur decreases by **2**, then you need 2 moles of HBr or HI
- if the oxidation state of sulphur decreases by **6**, then you need 6 moles of HI
- if the oxidation state of sulphur decreases by **8**, then you need 8 moles of HI

The greater the decrease in the oxidation state of the sulphur in sulphuric acid, the more it has been reduced. Using the observations, it can be deduced that the order of reducing power is *chloride < bromide < iodide*.

If you are asked to predict the reactions of the fluoride or astatide ion, then remember the trend. A fluoride ion will give similar reactions to a chloride ion, so you will need only one equation. An astatide ion will give similar reactions to an iodide ion, so you will need four equations.

Trends in properties of the halides (II)

This section concentrates on the use of silver nitrate to distinguish between the halide ions. You need to know the trend in solubility of silver halides in dilute and concentrated aqueous ammonia.

Use of silver nitrate solution as a test for halide ions

Silver nitrate solution is used to distinguish between fluoride, chloride, bromide and iodide ions. Silver fluoride is soluble, so no precipitate forms. The other halide ions form insoluble silver halide precipitates.

$Ag^+(aq) + Cl^-(aq) \longrightarrow AgCl(s)$ *white* precipitate

$Ag^+(aq) + Br^-(aq) \longrightarrow AgBr(s)$ *cream* precipitate

$Ag^+(aq) + I^-(aq) \longrightarrow AgI(s)$ *yellow* precipitate

Dilute nitric acid, HNO_3, is added to the halide solution to prevent the formation of other precipitates, such as Ag_2CO_3. Carbonates dissolve in acidic solution.

$CO_3^{2-} + 2H^+ \longrightarrow CO_2 + H_2O$

Using ammonia solution to distinguish between silver halides

Dilute and concentrated aqueous ammonia are used to distinguish between the silver halide precipitates.

- AgCl is soluble in dilute and concentrated $NH_3(aq)$.
- AgBr is insoluble in dilute but soluble in concentrated $NH_3(aq)$.
- AgI is insoluble in dilute and concentrated $NH_3(aq)$.

The precipitates that dissolve form soluble complex ions, for example $[Ag(NH_3)_2]^+$.

Uses of chlorine and the estimation of chlorate(I)

You have to be able to write equations for the redox reactions of chlorine with water and sodium hydroxide and to know the industrial importance of the products. You should be able to recall the equations for the reaction of NaClO solution (bleach) with potassium iodide and the reaction of the iodine produced with sodium thiosulphate solution. These equations are needed in calculations to estimate the amount of NaClO in samples of bleach.

The reaction of chlorine with water

Chlorine is used in the treatment of drinking water. It sterilises water by killing the bacteria in it. Chlorine reacts with water to form a mixture of hydrochloric acid (HCl) and chloric(I) acid (HClO).

$Cl_2 + H_2O \rightleftharpoons HCl + HClO$

When full range indicator is added, it initially turns red due to the presence of $H^+(aq)$. It then loses its colour due to the presence of ClO^- ions, which act as a bleach.

The reaction of chlorine with cold dilute sodium hydroxide

Sodium chlorate(I) solution (NaClO) is used as an active ingredient in bleach. It is formed by the reaction of chlorine with cold, dilute, aqueous sodium hydroxide.

$$Cl_2 + 2NaOH \longrightarrow NaCl + NaClO + H_2O$$

Disproportionation

The reactions of chlorine with water and with sodium hydroxide are examples of **disproportionation**, i.e. the simultaneous oxidation and reduction of the same species. In these reactions, the oxidation state of the chlorine increases from 0 to +1 (oxidation) and decreases from 0 to −1 (reduction).

$$Cl_2 + H_2O \longrightarrow HCl + HClO$$
$$0 \qquad\qquad\quad -1 \quad +1$$
$$Cl_2 + 2NaOH \longrightarrow NaCl + NaClO + H_2O$$
$$0 \qquad\qquad\quad -1 \quad +1$$

Estimating the amount of sodium chlorate(I) in bleach

Method

Take $10\,cm^3$ of concentrated bleach and dilute it with water to make up a $250\,cm^3$ solution. Take $25\,cm^3$ of this diluted bleach solution and add excess solid potassium iodide to produce an iodine solution. Titrate this iodine solution against a standard solution of sodium thiosulphate. Add starch (the end-point indicator) when the brown colour starts to fade, i.e. just before the end-point. A blue–black colour is produced. The accurate end-point for the titration is indicated by the blue–black solution becoming colourless.

Equations

You are expected to remember these two equations.

$$ClO^- + 2H^+ + 2I^- \longrightarrow Cl^- + H_2O + I_2$$
$$I_2 + 2S_2O_3^{2-} \longrightarrow 2I^- + S_4O_6^{2-}$$

Typical calculation

This calculation shows the procedure used for any titre value. It is important that you understand each step of the calculation.

$10\,cm^3$ of bleach, containing the active ingredient sodium chlorate(I), were made up to $250\,cm^3$ of solution with distilled water. Then, $25.0\,cm^3$ of this dilute solution were treated with an excess of acidified potassium iodide. The liberated iodine required $17.00\,cm^3$ of sodium thiosulphate solution of concentration $0.100\,mol\,dm^{-3}$. Calculate the concentration, in $g\,dm^{-3}$, of the sodium chlorate(I).

- Moles of thiosulphate used = MV/1000 = $\dfrac{0.1 \times 17}{1000} = 1.7 \times 10^{-3}$
  (M = molarity and V = titre)
- Moles of iodine = 8.5×10^{-4} (because the ratio of I_2 to $S_2O_3^{2-}$ is 1:2)
- Moles of ClO^- in $25\,cm^3$ = 8.5×10^{-4} (because the ratio of ClO^- to I_2 is 1:1)

- Moles of ClO^- in $250\,cm^3 = 8.5 \times 10^{-3}$
- Moles of ClO^- in $10\,cm^3$ of undiluted bleach $= 8.5 \times 10^{-3}$
- Moles of ClO^- in $1\,dm^3$ of undiluted bleach $= 0.85$
- Mass of NaClO in $1\,dm^3$ of undiluted bleach $= M_r \times 0.85$
- Mass of NaClO per $dm^3 = 74.5 \times 0.85 = 63.3\,g\,dm^{-3}$

Extraction of metals

This topic concentrates on the extraction of three common metals: iron, aluminium and titanium. It is important that you do not just consider them separately — you need to be able to compare and contrast the three extraction processes. This guide emphasises the comparisons.

The importance of metals

Metals have many desirable properties. Most are:
- strong
- ductile
- malleable
- good thermal conductors
- good electrical conductors

The occurrence of metals

The metals in the table below are some of the most common in the Earth's crust. You have to know how to extract these metals from their ores.

Metal	Common ore	Formula of oxide
Iron	Haematite	Fe_2O_3
Aluminium	Bauxite	Al_2O_3
Titanium	Rutile	TiO_2

Other commonly used metals, such as copper and nickel, are relatively rare in the Earth's crust. Their use is still possible, because they are found in high-grade ores in very specific locations.

Factors considered when extracting a metal from its ore

Cost of the reducing agent

Carbon (coke) is used in the extraction of iron. Coke is readily available, so it is a cheap reducing agent. Sodium is used in the extraction of titanium. Sodium is a very expensive reducing agent.

Cost of energy

The extraction of aluminium consumes large amounts of electricity and is only viable where electricity is relatively inexpensive.

Required purity of the metal

Titanium is very expensive to produce and the metal extracted must be free of impurities. The cost of the extraction process is justified by the high market price of the metal and the desirable properties of titanium, which is used as an engineering material.

Reduction of the metal ore to the metal

The three metals all occur as oxides. To produce the metal, the oxygen is removed, i.e. the ore is reduced, preferably using a cheap reducing agent such as carbon (coke).

The problem with carbon

Metal extracted	Will carbon work?	Explanation
Iron	Yes	The iron will be impure, but carbon impurities can be tolerated
Aluminium	No	Theoretically, all metal oxides can be reduced by carbon; however, the temperature required is too high to be economic
Titanium	No	Titanium cannot tolerate carbon impurities; it forms titanium carbide (TiC), which makes the metal very brittle: $$TiO_2 + 3C \longrightarrow TiC + 2CO$$

The type of reduction used in the extraction process

Metal extracted	Type of reduction	Reductant
Iron	Carbon reduction	Carbon (coke)
Aluminium	Electrolytic reduction	Electrons
Titanium	Active metal reduction	Sodium or magnesium

You need to be able to recall the detail of each of the three processes. However, the principles behind each extraction are more important. You should be able to extract information needed to answer a specific question. You may be asked for the raw materials, the equations, the conditions and the removal of impurities or the reasons why the metal is expensive to produce. It is essential that you can compare and contrast the methods of production.

Extraction of iron using carbon reduction

This is a *continuous* process. The raw materials (haematite, limestone and coke) are fed in at the top of a blast furnace.

Production of the high temperature
- High temperatures are produced by the reaction of the coke with hot air.
$$C + O_2 \longrightarrow CO_2$$

Production of the reducing agent
- The carbon dioxide produced reacts with the coke to produce carbon monoxide.
$$CO_2 + C \longrightarrow 2CO$$

Reduction of iron oxide
- Iron oxide is reduced by carbon or carbon monoxide.
$$Fe_2O_3 + 3C \longrightarrow 2Fe + 3CO$$
$$Fe_2O_3 + 3CO \longrightarrow 2Fe + 3CO_2$$

Removal of impurities
- Limestone removes acidic impurities.
- It decomposes at high temperatures, forming calcium oxide (lime) and carbon dioxide.
$$CaCO_3 \longrightarrow CaO + CO_2$$
- Calcium oxide is basic and reacts with acidic impurities such as SiO_2.
$$CaO + SiO_2 \longrightarrow CaSiO_3 \text{ (slag)}$$
  The slag produced is used in breezeblocks and insulation.

Conversion of iron to steel
- The final product of the blast furnace is impure iron.
- Impure iron is brittle due to impurities (4% carbon and some Si, S and P). Lowering the percentage of these impurities makes iron more malleable.
- Carbon is removed by blasting oxygen through the molten iron. Carbon reacts with oxygen to form carbon monoxide.
- Sulphur is removed by adding magnesium. Magnesium sulphide is formed.
- Silicon and phosphorus are removed by reacting with oxygen, then adding calcium oxide. Silicon and phosphorus oxides react with calcium oxide to form a slag, which floats above the iron.
- Steel is an iron–carbon alloy with low carbon content.

Extraction of aluminium using electrolytic reduction

This is a *continuous* process, with regular additions of aluminium oxide to the cells.

Choice of conditions
- The temperature needed to reduce Al_2O_3 with carbon is too high.
- Aluminium is extracted by the **electrolysis** of purified bauxite.
- The melting point of Al_2O_3 is too high to carry out the electrolysis, so it is dissolved in **molten cryolite** (Na_3AlF_6), which lowers its melting point.
- Large amounts of electricity are needed to keep the electrolyte molten at 970 °C in the electrolytic cells.
- Carbon electrodes are used.

Reactions at the electrodes
- Cathode: $Al^{3+} + 3e^- \longrightarrow Al$ (reduction)
- Anode: $2O^{2-} \longrightarrow O_2 + 4e^-$ (oxidation)
- The anodes need to be replaced regularly.
- The carbon anodes react with oxygen at high temperatures.

$$C + O_2 \longrightarrow CO_2$$

Extraction of titanium using active metal reduction

This is a **batch** process. The titanium is made one batch at a time — this is more costly than a continuous process.

Conversion of rutile to titanium(IV) chloride
- The raw materials are rutile, chlorine and coke.
- The temperature needed is 900 °C.

$$TiO_2 + 2C + 2Cl_2 \longrightarrow TiCl_4 + 2CO$$

Reduction of titanium(IV) chloride to titanium
- Titanium(IV) chloride is reduced using an active metal such as sodium or magnesium.
- The temperature varies from 550 °C to 1000 °C.
- An inert atmosphere of argon is essential to prevent impurities forming in the metal due to the presence of oxygen or nitrogen.

$$TiCl_4 + 4Na \longrightarrow Ti + 4NaCl$$
$$TiCl_4 + 2Mg \longrightarrow Ti + 2MgCl_2$$

Desirable properties of titanium
Titanium is a desirable engineering material because of its:
- low density
- high strength
- high resistance to corrosion

The high cost of production
Titanium is an abundant metal in the Earth's crust, but it is expensive to extract and its large-scale use is limited because:
- it has to be produced by active metal reduction to avoid contamination with impurities (such as carbon, nitrogen and oxygen), which makes the metal brittle
- it is produced by a batch process, which is expensive
- sodium and chlorine are expensive raw materials
- high temperatures are involved in both stages of production
- the titanium(IV) chloride produced in the first stage of the extraction reacts violently with water, so special precautions have to be taken
- an argon atmosphere is used to prevent oxidation in the second stage

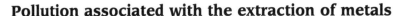

Pollution associated with the extraction of metals

You need to be aware of environmental problems associated with metal extraction. You should be able to recall the three main pollutants, their source and their effect on the environment. You will not be expected to give detailed answers.

Sulphur dioxide causes the production of **acid rain**, which damages plants, buildings and acidifies lakes. Many metal ores occur as sulphides. They are roasted in air to produce the oxides, which are then reduced to produce the metal. Roasting of sulphide ores causes sulphur dioxide pollution.

Carbon monoxide is a **toxic** gas produced in the extraction of all three metals above.

Carbon dioxide is a **greenhouse gas** produced by the burning of fossil fuels, such as coke in the blast furnace.

Recycling

Ideally, all metals should be recycled, but the cost of collection, transportation and separation of the scrap metal must be taken into account and compared with the cost of extraction of the metal from the ore.

Iron is the most extensively recycled metal because:
- scrap iron contains a higher percentage of iron than iron ore
- scrap iron can be made molten in the electric arc process — an electric arc passes between electrodes, generating high temperatures to melt the iron
- remelting scrap iron does not produce carbon dioxide, whereas the extraction of iron from its ore does
- it avoids the build-up of vast quantities of scrap metal
- iron objects are magnetic, so they can be easily separated from other waste

The extraction of aluminium is expensive, because electrolysis requires vast amounts of electricity. Re-melting aluminium cans saves 95% of the extraction energy. However, this energy saving must be balanced against the costs associated with collecting and separating scrap aluminium, which are considerable.

Questions
&
Answers

These questions are similar in style and content to those that you can expect in Unit Test 2. They have been designed to test all the key facts and concepts covered in Module 2.

Unit Test 2 is divided into sections A and B. Section A questions are structured, with spaces at the end of each question part for your response. Section B usually contains a longer question, which is also divided into sections. It is effectively a long structured question, but without spaces between each section for you to write your answer.

All the questions in this Question and Answer section are structured, without answer spaces. If a question is worth 12 marks, then you should expect to write no more than 12 sentences. The marking scheme identifies 12 key words or phrases that must be present for you to score 12 marks.

All the questions in this Question and Answer section are worth 30 marks. In Unit Test 2 it is rare to find one question concentrating on one topic. However, these 30 marks could represent three separate structured questions, each worth 10 marks, from separate papers.

In order to use this section effectively, you should:
- make sure you have revised the topic thoroughly before you attempt the question
- read the question carefully and then answer it under test conditions
- use the grade-A answer to assess the quality of your answer — the grade-A answer has been marked by an examiner, with ticks placed where the marks are scored
- read through the examiner's comments to see the common errors made by candidates and tips for improving your answers
- never underestimate the help of your teacher — if you do not understand some of the points made in the answers or the examiner's comments, then ask your teacher (or other students) to explain
- make sure that you concentrate on your weak areas when revising rather than on the topics that you understand

In addition to this guide, use as much material from the AQA exam board as possible. Answer as many past paper questions as you can and then use the mark schemes to grade your answers and analyse your mistakes. As a rough guide, you need to score 80% for a grade A, 70% for a grade B and 60% for a grade C.

Energetics

(1) (a) (i) Define the term *standard enthalpy of combustion*. (3 marks)

    (ii) Write an equation to describe the standard enthalpy of combustion of ethane, C_2H_6. (2 marks)

    (iii) Use the enthalpy of combustion data below to calculate the enthalpy of formation of ethane, C_2H_6.

        ● Enthalpy of combustion of carbon = $-394\ kJ\ mol^{-1}$

        ● Enthalpy of combustion of hydrogen = $-286\ kJ\ mol^{-1}$

        ● Enthalpy of combustion of ethane = $-1560\ kJ\ mol^{-1}$ (3 marks)

(b) (i) Define the term *standard enthalpy of formation*. (3 marks)

    (ii) Write an equation to describe the standard enthalpy of formation of ethanol, C_2H_5OH. (2 marks)

    (iii) Use the enthalpy of formation data below to calculate the enthalpy of combustion of ethanol, C_2H_5OH.

        ● Enthalpy of formation of ethanol = $-278\ kJ\ mol^{-1}$

        ● Enthalpy of formation of carbon dioxide = $-394\ kJ\ mol^{-1}$

        ● Enthalpy of formation of water = $-286\ kJ\ mol^{-1}$ (3 marks)

(c) The enthalpy of combustion of methanol can be estimated by using bond enthalpy data.

$$H-\underset{\underset{H}{|}}{\overset{\overset{H}{|}}{C}}-O-H + \tfrac{3}{2}\ O{=}O \longrightarrow O{=}C{=}O + 2\ \underset{H}{O}{\diagdown}_{H}$$

Bond	Bond enthalpy/kJ mol^{-1}
C–H	412
C–O	360
O–H	463
O=O	496
C=O	743

    Use the data above to estimate the enthalpy of combustion of methanol. (4 marks)

(d) In an experiment to determine the enthalpy of combustion of methanol, 0.55 g of liquid methanol (CH_3OH) was burned in a spirit burner, which was placed under an aluminium can containing 100 g of water. The initial temperature of the water was 19 °C and the final temperature was 40 °C. The specific heat capacity of water is $4.18\ kJ\ K^{-1}\ kg^{-1}$.

    (i) Calculate the heat energy absorbed by the water. (3 marks)

    (ii) Calculate the moles of methanol burned in the reaction. (2 marks)

    (iii) Calculate the enthalpy change for the reaction. (3 marks)

(iv) The theoretical standard enthalpy of combustion of methanol is −715 kJ mol⁻¹. Suggest two reasons why the answer in part (iii) is less exothermic than the theoretical value.

(2 marks)

Total: 30 marks

■ ■ ■

Grade-A answer to Question 1

(a) (i) The enthalpy change when 1 mole ✓ of a substance is completely burned in oxygen ✓ under standard conditions, i.e. 298 K and 100 kPa ✓.

e You must be able to recall definitions precisely.

(ii) $C_2H_6(g) + 3\frac{1}{2}O_2(g) \longrightarrow 2CO_2(g) + 3H_2O(l)$ ✓ ✓

e There is 1 mark for a balanced equation and 1 mark for the correct state symbols.

(iii) $2C + 3H_2 \longrightarrow C_2H_6$ ✓

$2CO_2 + 3H_2O$

$\Delta H_f = (2 \times -394) + (3 \times -286) - (-1560)$ ✓ $= -86$ kJ mol⁻¹ ✓

e A correct answer of −86 kJ mol⁻¹ scores 3 marks. If the answer is incorrect because of a careless arithmetical error then, provided you have shown your working, you will score 2 marks. If you have drawn the correct cycle but obtained an incorrect answer of +86 kJ mol⁻¹, then this would be marked as a chemical error and you would only score 1 mark for the cycle.

(b) (i) The enthalpy change when 1 mole ✓ of a compound is formed from its elements ✓ in their standard states ✓ at 298K and 100 kPa.

e Three key points are essential in this definition.

(ii) $2C(s) + 3H_2(g) + \frac{1}{2}O_2(g) \longrightarrow C_2H_5OH(l)$ ✓ ✓

e There is 1 mark for a balanced equation and 1 mark for the state symbols.

(iii) $C_2H_5OH + 3O_2 \longrightarrow 2CO_2 + 3H_2O$ ✓

$2C + 3H_2 + 3\frac{1}{2}O_2$

$\Delta H_c = (2 \times -394) + (3 \times -286) - (-278)$ ✓ $= -1368$ kJ mol⁻¹ ✓

e The same arguments apply as those in part (a) (iii). An alternative to the cycle would be the statement $\Delta H_r = \Sigma \Delta H_f$ products − $\Sigma \Delta H_f$ reactants.

(c) Energy needed to break bonds $= 3(C–H) + (C–O) + (O–H) + \frac{3}{2}(O=O)$

$= 3(412) + 360 + 463 + \frac{3}{2}(496)$

$= 2803$ kJ mol⁻¹ ✓

Energy produced forming bonds = 2(C=O) + 4(O–H)
$$= 2(743) + 4(463)$$
$$= 3338 \, kJ \, mol^{-1} \checkmark$$

Enthalpy change for the reaction = 2803 – 3338 $\checkmark$
$$= -535 \, kJ \, mol^{-1} \checkmark$$

e A correct answer of $-535 \, kJ \, mol^{-1}$ scores 4 marks. If you made a mistake calculating the energy needed to break the bonds or calculating the energy produced in forming new bonds, but the rest of the working was correct, then you would still score 3 marks.

(d) (i) The heat absorbed by the water:
$q = mc\Delta T \checkmark = 0.1 \times 4.18 \times 21 \checkmark = 8.78 \, kJ \checkmark$
(ii) The number of moles used:
$n = m/M_r \checkmark = 0.55/32 = 0.0172 \checkmark$
(iii) The enthalpy change:
$\Delta H = -q/n \checkmark = -8.78/0.0172 = - \checkmark 510 \, kJ \, mol^{-1} \checkmark$
(iv) The enthalpy change is less exothermic than expected due to heat loss to the surroundings $\checkmark$ and incomplete combustion of the alcohol $\checkmark$.

e In any calculation, you must show your working, because if you make one mistake you can still score 7 marks, provided that the rest of the calculation is correct. Two reasons are given for the value being less exothermic than expected. Alternative answers include the lack of stirring of the water and the fact that the heat capacity of the aluminium can is ignored.

Kinetics

(2) (a) (i) Using the axes shown, draw a Maxwell–Boltzman distribution curve for molecules of a gas at a particular temperature. Label this curve T_1. (3 marks)

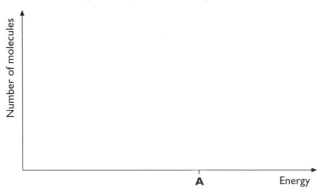

(ii) Label with the letter X the most probable energy of the molecules at the temperature T_1. (1 mark)

(iii) **How do the molecules in a gas exchange energy?** (1 mark)

(iv) **What effect, if any, does this exchange of energy have on the distribution of molecular energies shown by curve T_1?** (1 mark)

(v) **Explain why curve T_1 starts at the origin.** (1 mark)

(vi) **What is represented by the total area under curve T_1?** (1 mark)

(b) (i) **Draw a second curve on the same axes, labelling it T_2, for the same sample of gaseous molecules at a higher temperature.** (2 marks)

(ii) **Why is the total area under curve T_1 the same as the total area under T_2.** (1 mark)

(iii) **By reference to the curves, state and explain in molecular terms the effect of increasing the temperature on the rate of reaction.** (3 marks)

(c) **Give two requirements for a reaction to occur between molecules in the gas phase.** (2 marks)

(d) **The letter A on the horizontal axis represents the activation energy for the reaction.**

(i) **Explain the meaning of the term *activation energy*.** (2 marks)

(ii) **Shade on the graph the area that represents the number of particles with energy greater than the energy of activation at the temperature T_1.** (1 mark)

(iii) **What effect, if any, does an increase in temperature have on the activation energy?** (1 mark)

(e) (i) **Explain the meaning of the term *catalyst* and explain the general role of a catalyst in a chemical reaction.** (4 marks)

(ii) **Mark on the horizontal axis a possible activation energy when a catalyst is present. Label it B.** (1 mark)

(iii) **State and explain in molecular terms the effect of a catalyst on the rate of reaction.** (3 marks)

(iv) **Give an example of a catalyst and the reaction that it catalyses.** (2 marks)

Total: 30 marks

■ ■ ■

Grade-A answer to Question 2

(a) (i)

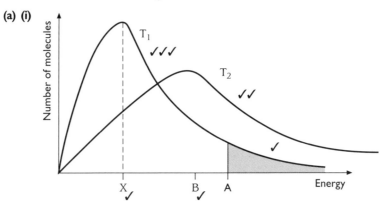

✎ The curve T_1 must start at the origin, have a good shape and not touch the x-axis.

(ii) See diagram

✎ The peak of the curve shows the most probable energy. However, you must label the energy axis and not the peak.

(iii) They exchange energy by collision ✓.
(iv) None ✓

✎ There is no change, because the collisions are perfectly elastic.

(v) No particles have zero energy ✓.
(vi) The total number of particles in the sample ✓.
(b) (i) See diagram

✎ There are 2 marks for curve T_2. The peak of the curve must be displaced to the right and it should be lower than the peak of T_1.

(ii) The total number of particles in the sample is the same ✓.
(iii) The rate increases ✓ because more particles ✓ have energy greater than the energy of activation ✓.

✎ The explanation for the effect of temperature can be brief.

(c) They must collide ✓ and they must possess energy greater than the energy of activation ✓.

✎ Another possible answer is that they must have the correct orientation.

(d) (i) Energy of activation is the minimum ✓ energy needed to cause a reaction ✓.

✎ Minimum is the key word in this definition.

(ii) See diagram.
(iii) Temperature has no effect on the energy of activation ✓.

✎ Many students think that an increase in temperature leads to a lowering in the energy of activation.

(e) (i) A catalyst speeds up the rate ✓ of the reaction, but itself remains chemically unchanged ✓. It provides an alternative route ✓ with a lower energy of activation ✓.

✎ Some catalysts can slow down the rate of a reaction, so the word 'alters' is an alternative to speeds up.

(ii) See diagram.

✎ B can appear anywhere to the left of A on the energy axis.

(iii) The catalyst increases the rate ✓, because more particles ✓ have energy greater than the energy of activation ✓.

☑ The explanation for the effect of a catalyst can be brief.

(iv) Iron ✓ in the production of ammonia (Haber process), i.e.
$$N_2 + 3H_2 \longrightarrow 2NH_3 \checkmark$$

☑ Other suitable catalysts are acceptable, but they must be related to the correct process. Manganese(IV) oxide speeds up the decomposition of hydrogen peroxide, vanadium(V) oxide is used in the Contact process and nickel is used in the hydrogenation of alkenes.

Equilibria

(3) (a) Each of the equations in the table below, labelled **A** to **E**, represents a dynamic equilibrium.

A	$N_2(g) + O_2(g) \rightleftharpoons 2NO(g)$	$\Delta H = +180\,kJ\,mol^{-1}$
B	$N_2O_4(g) \rightleftharpoons 2NO_2(g)$	$\Delta H = +58\,kJ\,mol^{-1}$
C	$2SO_2(g) + O_2(g) \rightleftharpoons 2SO_3(g)$	$\Delta H = -196\,kJ\,mol^{-1}$
D	$N_2(g) + 3H_2(g) \rightleftharpoons 2NH_3(g)$	$\Delta H = -92\,kJ\,mol^{-1}$
E	$H_2(g) + I_2(g) \rightleftharpoons 2HI(g)$	$\Delta H = -11\,kJ\,mol^{-1}$

(i) Explain what is meant by the term *dynamic equilibrium*. (3 marks)

(ii) Use the appropriate letter(s) to identify the reactions in which the equlibrium yield:
  • increases as the temperature decreases
  • increases as the pressure decreases
  • does not change with a change in pressure, but increases with an increase in temperature (5 marks)

(iii) State what effect, if any, the addition of a platinum catalyst would have on the position of the equilibrium in reaction **C**. (1 mark)

(iv) State what effect, if any, the removal of NH_3 would have on the position of the equilibrium in reaction **D**. (1 mark)

(b) The equilibrium reaction below is carried out at 325 °C in the presence of a nickel catalyst.
$$CO(g) + 3H_2(g) \rightleftharpoons CH_4(g) + H_2O(g) \quad \Delta H = -206.1\,kJ\,mol^{-1}$$

(i) State and explain how the equilibrium position would change if:
  • the temperature of the reaction was increased
  • the total pressure was increased (6 marks)

(ii) State the effect of the nickel catalyst on:
  • the rate of the forward and backward reactions at equilibrium
  • the equilibrium position (3 marks)

   (iii) **State the effect on the equilibrium position of removing water from the reaction mixture. Explain your answer.** (2 marks)
   (iv) **Give one reason why, in practice, the reaction is carried out at a high temperature.** (1 mark)
  (c) **Explain why a temperature of 723 K and a pressure of 2.5×10^4 kPa are chosen as the compromise conditions for the synthesis of ammonia in the Haber process.**

$$N_2(g) + 3H_2(g) \rightleftharpoons 2NH_3(g) \quad \Delta H = -92 \text{ kJ mol}^{-1}$$
                      (8 marks)
                   Total: 30 marks

■ ■ ■

Grade-A answer to Question 3

(a) (i) A dynamic equilibrium is a continuous ✓ reaction in which the rate of the forward reaction equals the rate of the backward reaction ✓. This means there is no net change in the concentration of the reactants or the products ✓.

⊘ It is essential to recall these three key points to be awarded full marks.

 (ii) C, D and E ✓✓✓
   B ✓
   A ✓

⊘ You are not required to write explanations here. The reactions C, D and E are all exothermic reactions. A decrease in temperature leads to an increase in yield as the equilibrium position shifts to the right-hand side to oppose the change. In reaction B, a decrease in pressure increases the yield, because there are more moles on the right-hand side. The equilibrium position will move towards this side to oppose the change. Reactions A and E are both unaffected by pressure because they have the same number of moles of reactants and products. However, only reaction A has a higher yield at a higher temperature, because it is endothermic.

 (iii) None ✓

⊘ Only a brief statement is required.

 (iv) It shifts to the right-hand side ✓.

⊘ Only a brief statement is required.

(b) (i) An increase in temperature would cause the equilibrium position to shift to the left-hand side ✓ in order to decrease the temperature and oppose the change ✓. The system moves in the endothermic back direction ✓.

  An increase in total pressure would cause the equilibrium position to shift to the right-hand side ✓ in order to decrease the pressure and oppose the change ✓. The system moves to the side with the fewest moles ✓ (there are four moles of reactants and two moles of products).

ⓔ When explaining the effect of temperature and pressure on a system at equilibrium, always include three key points for each factor: the effect on the equilibrium position; what happens to oppose the change; and the exothermic or endothermic nature (when discussing temperature), or the number of moles on each side (when discussing pressure).

(ii) A nickel catalyst increases the rate ✓ of the forward and backward reactions equally ✓. The catalyst has no effect ✓ on the equilibrium position.

ⓔ The word 'equally' is very important and is often missed.

(iii) Removing water shifts the equilibrium position to the right-hand side ✓ in order to replace the water and oppose the change ✓.

ⓔ When a product is removed, the system will always move to replace it.

(iv) A high temperature is used to increase the rate ✓ of the reaction.

(c) The reaction is exothermic in the forward direction ✓, so a low temperature favours a high yield ✓. However, at low temperature, the reaction rate is low ✓ because fewer particles have energy greater than the energy of activation ✓. A moderate temperature is required as a compromise.

The reaction involves a decrease in the number of moles in the forward direction ✓, so a high pressure favours a high yield ✓. A high pressure also produces a high reaction rate ✓, because there is a greater collision frequency ✓. However, a high pressure increases the costs ✓ of building the plant and is expensive to maintain. A moderate pressure is used as a compromise.

ⓔ When answering questions of this type, always think of the three key factors: yield, rate and cost. You then need to discuss the optimum temperature and pressure for each of these factors. The conclusion is usually that a compromise set of conditions is required. In the answer there are nine scoring points. You need eight of these for full marks.

Redox reactions

(4) (a) Deduce the oxidation state of nitrogen in the following species:
- **NO**
- **NO_2**
- **NO_2^+**
- **NO_3^-**
- **NH_3**
- **NH_4^+** (6 marks)

(b) Which of the following reactions, involving nitrogen compounds, are examples of redox reactions?

(i) $HNO_3 + 2H_2SO_4 \longrightarrow 2HSO_4^- + H_3O^+ + NO_2^+$

(ii) $Cu + 2NO_3^- + 4H^+ \longrightarrow Cu^{2+} + 2NO_2 + 2H_2O$

(iii) $2NH_3 + H_2SO_4 \longrightarrow 2NH_4^+ + SO_4^{2-}$

(iv) $HNO_2 + Br_2 + H_2O \longrightarrow NO_3^- + 3H^+ + 2Br^-$

If the reaction is not a redox reaction, then indicate this by stating 'not redox'. In the redox reactions, state whether the nitrogen species has been oxidised or reduced during the reaction. (6 marks)

(c) For each equation below, identify the element that has been oxidised and state the oxidation state of this element before and after the reaction.

(i) $3CuO + 2NH_3 \longrightarrow 3Cu + N_2 + 3H_2O$ (3 marks)

(ii) $8HI + H_2SO_4 \longrightarrow 4I_2 + H_2S + 4H_2O$ (3 marks)

(iii) $SO_2 + Br_2 + 2H_2O \longrightarrow 2HBr + H_2SO_4$ (3 marks)

(d) Deduce half-equations for the following reactions:

(i) the oxidation of an iodide ion (I^-) to iodine (I_2) (1 mark)

(ii) the reduction of sulphuric acid (H_2SO_4) to sulphur dioxide (SO_2) (1 mark)

(iii) the reduction of an iodate(V) ion (IO_3^-) to iodine (I_2) (1 mark)

(e) Use the half-equations in part (d) to deduce the full redox equation for the oxidation of an iodide ion by:

(i) concentrated sulphuric acid (2 marks)

(ii) a solution containing iodate(V) ions (2 marks)

(f) The following is an equation for a redox reaction:

$$5Fe^{2+} + MnO_4^- + 8H^+ \longrightarrow 5Fe^{3+} + Mn^{2+} + 4H_2O$$

Identify the element being reduced in this reaction and write a half-equation for the reduction of the species containing this element. (2 marks)

Total: 30 marks

■ ■ ■

Grade-A answer to Question 4

(a) +2 ✓, +4 ✓, +5 ✓, +5 ✓, −3 ✓, −3 ✓

e No working out needs to be shown to achieve full marks. Oxygen is more electro-negative than nitrogen, so it has an oxidation state of −2. Hydrogen is less electro-negative than nitrogen, so it has an oxidation state of +1. The sum of the oxidation states in a compound is zero and the sum of the oxidation states in an ion is equal to the overall charge on the ion.

(b) (i) Not redox ✓

e The oxidation states are +5 and +5

(ii) Redox ✓; nitrogen is reduced ✓.

e The oxidation states are +5 and +4

(iii) Not redox ✓

🖉 The oxidation states are −3 and −3

(iv) Redox ✓; nitrogen is oxidised ✓.

🖉 The oxidation states are +3 and +5

🖉 No explanations are needed to achieve full marks. If the oxidation state of an element decreases, then it has been reduced; if the oxidation state increases, then it has been oxidised.

(c) **(i)** Nitrogen ✓, −3 ✓, 0 ✓
 (ii) Iodine ✓, −1 ✓, 0 ✓
 (iii) Sulphur ✓, +4 ✓, +6 ✓

🖉 Full marks are only awarded if the changes in the oxidation states are related to the correct element.

(d) **(i)** $2I^- \longrightarrow I_2 + 2e^-$ ✓
 (ii) $H_2SO_4 + 2H^+ + 2e^- \longrightarrow SO_2 + 2H_2O$ ✓

🖉 An alternative half-equation is $SO_4^{2-} + 4H^+ + 2e^- \longrightarrow SO_2 + 2H_2O$.

 (iii) $IO_3^- + 6H^+ + 5e^- \longrightarrow \frac{1}{2}I_2 + 3H_2O$ ✓

🖉 An alternative half-equation is $2IO_3^- + 12H^+ + 10e^- \longrightarrow I_2 + 6H_2O$.

(e) **(i)** $2HI + H_2SO_4 \longrightarrow I_2 + SO_2 + 2H_2O$ ✓ ✓

🖉 There must be no electrons in the final redox equation. The reaction of I^- and H_2SO_4 just involves adding the two half-equations in (d) (i) and (d) (ii) together because the number of electrons is the same. Two other acceptable answers would be:
$$2H^+ + 2I^- + H_2SO_4 \longrightarrow I_2 + SO_2 + 2H_2O$$
$$4H^+ + 2I^- + SO_4^{2-} \longrightarrow I_2 + SO_2 + 2H_2O$$

 (ii) $5I^- + IO_3^- + 6H^+ \longrightarrow 3I_2 + 3H_2O$ ✓ ✓

🖉 Once again, there must be no electrons in the final redox equation. When adding the half-equations (d) (i) and (d) (iii) together for the reaction of I^- and IO_3^-, the iodide equation must be multiplied by $2\frac{1}{2}$ to give $5I^- \longrightarrow 2\frac{1}{2}I_2 + 5e^-$. Alternatively, you can multiply the iodide half-equation by 5 and the iodate(V) equation by 2 to produce the overall equation $10I^- + 2IO_3^- + 12H^+ \longrightarrow 6I_2 + 6H_2O$, but this must then be divided by 2 to achieve the final mark.

(f) Manganese is reduced ✓.
 $$MnO_4^- + 8H^+ + 5e^- \longrightarrow Mn^{2+} + 4H_2O \text{ ✓}$$

🖉 In order to create the half-equation, follow the basic principles outlined below.
 • List the species reduced: $MnO_4^- \longrightarrow Mn^{2+}$
 • Add H_2O: $MnO_4^- \longrightarrow Mn^{2+} + 4H_2O$
 • Add H^+: $MnO_4^- + 8H^+ \longrightarrow Mn^{2+} + 4H_2O$
 • Add electrons: $MnO_4^- + 8H^+ + 5e^- \longrightarrow Mn^{2+} + 4H_2O$

Group 7: the halogens

(5) (a) (i) State and explain the trend in the electronegativity of the halogens. (4 marks)
   (ii) State the name of the halogen with the lowest boiling point and briefly
        explain your answer. (3 marks)
   (b) (i) Describe, with the aid of an equation and observations, the reaction
        that occurs when gaseous chlorine is bubbled through an aqueous
        solution of sodium bromide. (2 marks)
   (ii) Write an equation for the reaction of chlorine with cold, dilute, aqueous
        sodium hydroxide and state the oxidation state of chlorine in each of
        the products. (3 marks)
   (iii) Chlorine also reacts with hot aqueous sodium hydroxide, according
        to the following equation:
        $$3Cl_2 + 6NaOH \longrightarrow 5NaCl + NaClO_3 + 3H_2O$$
        Name the compound $NaClO_3$. (2 marks)
   (iv) Sodium fluoride reacts with concentrated sulphuric acid. Predict the
        equation for the reaction and give two observations. (3 marks)
   (c) Deduce the oxidation states of the elements that have been reduced and
        oxidised in the following equation: (4 marks)
        $$2HBr + H_2SO_4 \longrightarrow Br_2 + SO_2 + 2H_2O$$
   (d) Explain why an iodide ion is a stronger reducing agent than a bromide
        ion. (3 marks)
   (e) Explain how separate solutions of sodium fluoride, sodium chloride and
        sodium bromide could be distinguished using solutions of aqueous silver
        nitrate and aqueous ammonia. (6 marks)

Total: 30 marks

■ ■ ■

Grade-A answer to Question 5

(a) (i) Electronegativity decreases ✓ down the group because the atomic
radius increases ✓ down the group. There are more shielding ✓ electrons,
which means there is less attraction for the electron density in a covalent
bond ✓.

An incorrect statement of increasing electronegativity would be marked as a chemical
error and no marks would be awarded for this answer. The addition of more shells is
an alternative to a larger atomic radius. It is essential that you refer to a covalent bond
to be awarded the final mark. The attraction for a bonding pair of electrons is an
alternative answer for the final mark.

(ii) Fluorine ✓ has the lowest boiling point because it has the smallest molecules ✓
with the weakest van der Waals forces ✓.

It is important to mention molecules, to emphasise that it is the forces between the molecules that are important. It is not the forces between the atoms; this would be marked as a chemical error.

(b) (i) $Cl_2 + 2NaBr \longrightarrow Br_2 + 2NaCl$ ✓
The displaced bromine produces a yellow solution ✓.

🅮 An ionic equation is acceptable ($Cl_2 + 2Br^- \longrightarrow 2Cl^- + Br_2$) and an orange solution is an alternative to yellow. Orange fumes or a brown solution are not acceptable.

(ii) $Cl_2 + 2NaOH \longrightarrow NaCl + NaClO + H_2O$ ✓
The oxidation state of chlorine in NaCl is -1 ✓ and in NaClO is $+1$ ✓.

🅮 An ionic equation, i.e. $Cl_2 + 2OH^- \longrightarrow Cl^- + ClO^- + H_2O$, is acceptable.

(iii) Sodium chlorate(V) ✓ ✓

🅮 If NaClO is called sodium chlorate(I), then you should be able to predict the name of $NaClO_3$. Sodium chlorate would be awarded 1 mark, but the (V) is essential for the second mark.

(iv) $NaF + H_2SO_4 \longrightarrow NaHSO_4 + HF$ ✓
Exothermic reaction ✓
Misty, white fumes evolved ✓

🅮 An alternative equation is $2NaF + H_2SO_4 \longrightarrow Na_2SO_4 + 2HF$. Another possible observation is fizzing or frothing.

(c) Sulphur is reduced: $+6$ ✓ to $+4$ ✓
Bromine is oxidised: -1 ✓ to 0 ✓

🅮 You must relate the oxidation states to the correct element to be awarded full marks. If you give only the oxidation states, then a maximum of 2 marks would be awarded.

(d) Iodide ions have a larger ionic radius ✓. A larger number of shells results in more shielding ✓ of the outer electron, which is more readily lost ✓ to another species.

🅮 If you mention atomic radius, this will be marked as a chemical error and no marks will be awarded for this section. 'Less attraction' is an alternative to 'more readily lost'.

(e) The addition of silver nitrate solution to NaF(aq) produces no precipitate ✓.
The addition of silver nitrate solution to NaCl(aq) produces a white precipitate ✓. This precipitate is readily soluble in dilute aqueous ammonia ✓.
The addition of silver nitrate solution to NaBr(aq) produces a cream precipitate ✓. This precipitate is insoluble in dilute aqueous ammonia ✓ but soluble in concentrated aqueous ammonia ✓.

🅮 It is essential that you specify *dilute* or *concentrated* when using aqueous ammonia. 'The precipitate is only partially soluble in dilute ammonia' is an alternative answer in the silver bromide section.

Extraction of metals

(6) The metals iron, aluminium and titanium occur in ores, which are abundant in the Earth's crust.

   (a) (i)   Name the ores that contain these metals. (3 marks)

   (ii) Which element is combined with the metals in these ores? (1 mark)

   (iii) What type of chemical reaction is always involved in the extraction of the metal from its ore? (1 mark)

   (iv) State three different methods for the extraction of these metals from their purified ores. In each case, write an equation describing the production of the metal. (6 marks)

   (v)   For each metal, indicate two factors that are important in choosing this method of extraction on an industrial scale. (6 marks)

   (vi) State three possible pollution problems that may arise in the extraction of these metals. (3 marks)

   (b) (i)   Explain why iron and aluminium are commonly used metals, despite iron being prone to rusting and aluminium being expensive to extract. (4 marks)

   (ii) Explain why some metallic elements that have a low abundance in the Earth's crust are still used more commonly than abundant metals such as titanium. (2 marks)

   (c) (i)   Give *three* reasons why iron is the most extensively recycled metal. (3 marks)

   (ii) Reprocessing aluminium can save up to 95% of the energy costs associated with the extraction of the metal from its ore. Why is recycling of aluminium not as extensive as recycling of iron? (1 mark)

Total: 30 marks

■ ■ ■

Grade-A answer to Question 6

(a) (i)   Haematite ✓ contains iron, bauxite ✓ contains aluminium and rutile ✓ contains titanium.

e Alternative answers include magnetite for iron and ilmenite for titanium.

   (ii) Oxygen ✓

e Oxygen is the only acceptable answer.

   (iii) Reduction ✓

e Redox is not acceptable.

   (iv) Carbon reduction ✓ : $Fe_2O_3 + 3CO \longrightarrow 2Fe + 3CO_2$ ✓

e An alternative equation is $Fe_2O_3 + 3C \longrightarrow 2Fe + 3CO$.

Electrolytic reduction ✓: $Al^{3+} + 3e^- \longrightarrow Al$ ✓
Active metal reduction ✓: $TiCl_4 + 4Na \longrightarrow 4NaCl + Ti$ ✓

e The equation for the reduction of titanium chloride with magnesium as the reducing agent is $TiCl_4 + 2Mg \longrightarrow Ti + 2MgCl_2$, which is an alternative answer.

(v) Iron — carbon impurities can be tolerated in the metal ✓. The iron ore can be reduced cheaply using carbon ✓.
   Aluminium — the temperature needed for carbon reduction is too high ✓. The desirable properties of aluminium justify the expensive electrolytic process ✓.
   Titanium — the titanium produced has to be pure ✓. Carbon reduction would give TiC, which is brittle ✓.

e This is a difficult question and there will be considerable variation in candidates' answers. Examiners often wait to see the variety of answers submitted and then they meet after the exam to decide what is acceptable.

(vi) The possible problems could be sulphur dioxide (leading to acid rain) ✓, carbon dioxide (a greenhouse gas) ✓ and carbon monoxide (toxic) ✓.

e It is essential for the pollution problem to be related to the pollutant, for a mark to be awarded. The question asks you to *state* the problems, not *describe* them, so do not include too much detail.

(b) (i) Both metals are very abundant and widely distributed ✓. Iron is cheap to extract ✓ and can be alloyed with other metals to make it strong and resistant to corrosion ✓. Aluminium has a low density ✓ and is corrosion-resistant ✓.

e 5 marks are shown here, but a maximum of 4 marks is awarded.

(ii) Some metals occur in concentrated ores ✓. They may be reduced cheaply using carbon ✓, in contrast to titanium which is very expensive to extract.

e 1 mark would be awarded simply for stating that titanium is expensive to extract.

(c) (i) Iron is recycled extensively because scrap iron contains a higher percentage of iron than iron ore ✓. Also, melting scrap steel does not produce carbon dioxide, whereas the extraction of iron from its ore does ✓. Recycling avoids the build-up of vast quantities of scrap metal ✓.

e The reasons given are the most obvious. Another possible answer is that iron is magnetic, and so is easily separated.

(ii) Recycling of aluminium is limited by the cost of collecting, transporting and separating the metal ✓.

e The cost of recycling any metal must always be balanced by considering energy savings, pollution problems, cost of collection, transport and separation.

Test 2

Energetics

(1) (a) (i) Define Hess's law. (2 marks)

   (ii) Use Hess's law to deduce the value of the unknown enthalpy change in
   the cycle below.

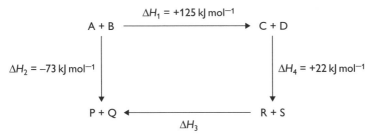

$\Delta H_1 = +125$ kJ mol^{-1}

A + B $\longrightarrow$ C + D

$\Delta H_2 = -73$ kJ mol^{-1} $\Delta H_4 = +22$ kJ mol^{-1}

P + Q $\longleftarrow$ R + S
ΔH_3

(1 mark)

(b) (i) Write equations to describe the standard enthalpy of formation of the
   following compounds:
   - butane, C_4H_{10}
   - calcium carbonate, $CaCO_3$
   - ammonia, NH_3 (6 marks)

   (ii) Use the combustion data below to calculate the enthalpy of formation
   of butane, C_4H_{10}.
   - Enthalpy of combustion of carbon = -394 kJ mol^{-1}
   - Enthalpy of combustion of hydrogen = -286 kJ mol^{-1}
   - Enthalpy of combustion of butane = -2877 kJ mol^{-1} (3 marks)

(c) Calculate the enthalpy change for the thermal decomposition of potassium
   hydrogencarbonate, using the enthalpy of formation data below.
   $$2KHCO_3(s) \longrightarrow K_2CO_3(s) + H_2O(g) + CO_2(g)$$

Compound	ΔH_f/kJ mol^{-1}
$KHCO_3$	-959
K_2CO_3	-1146
H_2O	-242
CO_2	-394

(3 marks)

(d) Use the enthalpy of formation data below to calculate the enthalpy change
   for the following reaction:
   $$2H_2O_2(l) + N_2H_4(l) \longrightarrow 4H_2O(g) + N_2(g)$$
   - Enthalpy of formation of hydrogen peroxide, $H_2O_2 = -188$ kJ mol^{-1}
   - Enthalpy of formation of hydrazine, $N_2H_4 = +50.4$ kJ mol^{-1}
   - Enthalpy of formation of steam, $H_2O(g) = -242$ kJ mol^{-1} (3 marks)

(e) Calculate the standard enthalpy of formation of hydrogen chloride gas, using the
   bond enthalpy data below.
   Bond enthalpies in kJ mol^{-1}: H–H = 436, Cl–Cl = 242, H–Cl = 431 (3 marks)

63

(f) In an insulated container, 50 cm³ of 2.0 M nitric acid (HNO₃) were added to 50 cm³ of 2.0 M sodium hydroxide (NaOH). The initial temperature of both solutions was 18 °C and the maximum temperature observed during the reaction was 31.5 °C. The heat capacity of water is 4.18 kJ K⁻¹ kg⁻¹.

    (i) Write an equation, including state symbols, for the reaction of nitric acid with sodium hydroxide. (2 marks)

    (ii) Calculate the temperature rise for the experiment. (1 mark)

    (iii) Calculate the heat energy absorbed by the solution formed, assuming it has the same heat capacity as water. (2 marks)

    (iv) Calculate the number of moles of water formed in the reaction, which is the same as the number of moles of acid used. (2 marks)

    (v) Calculate the standard enthalpy of neutralisation, which is the enthalpy change for the formation of one mole of water when an acid neutralises an alkali. (2 marks)

Total: 30 marks

■ ■ ■

Grade-A answer to Question 1

(a) (i) The enthalpy change for a reaction is constant ✓ and independent of the route taken ✓, provided the initial and final states are the same.

🅮 You must be able to recall definitions precisely.

    (ii) $\Delta H_3 = -220$ kJ mol⁻¹ ✓

🅮 The question asks for the enthalpy change from 'R + S' to 'P + Q'. If the alternative route is followed, then +22 becomes −22, +125 becomes −125 and −73 remains as −73, which gives a total of −220 kJ mol⁻¹. If you change the direction of the arrow, then remember to change the sign of the enthalpy change.

(b) (i) $4C(s) + 5H_2(g) \longrightarrow C_4H_{10}(g)$ ✓ ✓

    $Ca(s) + C(s) + 1\frac{1}{2}O_2(g) \longrightarrow CaCO_3(s)$ ✓ ✓

    $\frac{1}{2}N_2(g) + 1\frac{1}{2}H_2(g) \longrightarrow NH_3(g)$ ✓ ✓

🅮 In all the questions of this type, there is 1 mark for the balanced equation, which in this case must lead to the formation of only one mole of the product. The second mark is for the correct state symbols.

    (ii) $4C(s) + 5H_2(g) \longrightarrow C_4H_{10}(g)$

                   ↘   ↙   ✓

        $4CO_2(g) + 5H_2O(l)$

    $\Delta H_f = (4 \times -394) + (5 \times -286) - (-2877)$ ✓

        $= -129$ kJ mol⁻¹ ✓

✐ The answer of −129 achieves 3 marks. An incorrect answer produced as a result of an arithmetical error is worth 2 marks. The incorrect answer of +129 only achieves 1 mark.

(c) $2KHCO_3(s) \longrightarrow K_2CO_3(s) + H_2O(g) + CO_2(g)$

   $\quad$ 2(−959) $\qquad$ −1146 $\quad$ −242 $\quad$ −394

   $\Delta H_r = \Sigma \Delta H_f$ products − $\Sigma \Delta H_f$ reactants ✓

   $\qquad = -1146 - 242 - 394 - 2(-959)$ ✓

   $\qquad = +136$ kJ mol^{-1} ✓

✐ The answer of +136 achieves 3 marks. If the statement or cycle is given but the answer is −136, then only 1 mark is awarded. If you fail to multiply the −959 by 2, then the answer is −823 kJ and it is worth 2 marks. If you fail to change the sign of the −959, then the answer is −3700 kJ and the only mark will be awarded for the cycle or the statement.

(d) $2H_2O_2 + N_2H_4 \longrightarrow 4H_2O + N_2$

   $\quad$ 2(−188) +50.4 $\qquad$ 4(−242) $\quad$ 0

   $\Delta H_r = \Sigma \Delta H_f$ products − $\Sigma \Delta H_f$ reactants ✓

   $\qquad = 4(-242) - 2(-188) - (+50.4)$ ✓

   $\qquad = -642.4$ kJ mol^{-1} ✓

✐ The answer of −642.4 achieves 3 marks. Failing to multiply −242 by 4 and −188 by 2 produces an answer of −104.4, which is worth 1 mark. Failing to multiply one of the numbers produces answers of either −830.4 or +83.6, which would be worth 2 marks. An answer of +642.4 is only worth 1 mark.

(e) $\frac{1}{2}H_2(g) + \frac{1}{2}Cl_2(g) \longrightarrow HCl(g)$

$\qquad\qquad\qquad\qquad$ ✓

$\qquad\quad H(g) + Cl(g)$

   $\Delta H_f = \frac{1}{2}(436) + \frac{1}{2}(242) - 431$ ✓

   $\qquad = -92$ kJ mol^{-1} ✓

✐ A common incorrect answer is −184 kJ mol^{-1}, based on the equation:

   $\qquad$ H−H + Cl−Cl $\longrightarrow$ 2H−Cl

This equation can be used, provided that the final answer of −184 is divided by 2. The enthalpy of formation is defined as the enthalpy change when one mole of the compound is formed from its elements in their standard states.

(f) (i) $HNO_3(aq) + NaOH(aq) \longrightarrow NaNO_3(aq) + H_2O(l)$ ✓ ✓

✐ There is 1 mark for the equation and 1 mark for the state symbols.

$\quad$ **(ii)** $\Delta T = 13.5°C$ ✓

$\quad$ **(iii)** $q = mc\Delta T$ ✓ $= 0.1 \times 4.18 \times 13.5 = 5.64$ kJ ✓

(iv) $n = MV/1000$ ✓ $= 2 \times 50/1000 = 0.1$ mol ✓

(v) $\Delta H = -q/n$ ✓ $= -5.64/0.1 = -56.4$ kJ mol^{-1} ✓

📝 It is essential that you show your working, so that consequential marks can be awarded after careless mistakes have been made.

Kinetics

(2) (a) (i) Draw a Maxwell–Boltzman curve for a sample of gas at a temperature, T_1. On the same axes, draw a second curve for the same sample of gas at a lower temperature and label this T_2. Label the curves and the axes clearly. (4 marks)

(ii) Suggest how the curve at T_1 would change if a catalyst was present and if a larger mass of gas was used. (3 marks)

(b) Give *three* ways in which the rate of reaction could be increased between a solid and a substance in solution other than by the addition of a catalyst. For each method, explain why the rate of the reaction increases. (9 marks)

(c) At 20 °C, an excess of calcium carbonate was added to 100 cm^3 of 0.1 M hydrochloric acid in a flask on an electronic balance. The balance was immediately set to zero. The mass of the reaction mixture was monitored over a period of time.

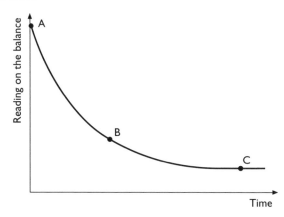

(i) Explain how the initial rate of this reaction could be determined. (2 marks)

(ii) Compare the rate of reaction at the points labelled A, B and C on the graph. Explain these rates in terms of collision theory. (6 marks)

(iii) Predict the shape of the curve that would be obtained if the excess calcium carbonate had been added to 100 cm^3 of 0.1 M hydrochloric acid that had been warmed to 40 °C. Briefly explain your answer. (4 marks)

(d) The reaction of calcium carbonate can also be monitored by recording the volume of carbon dioxide evolved over a period of time. The original reaction, where excess calcium carbonate was added to 100 cm^3 of 0.1 M hydrochloric acid at 20 °C, gave curve 2 on the graph below.

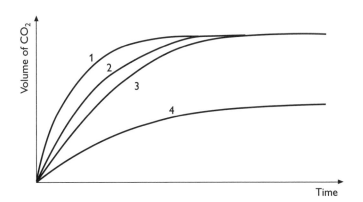

Which one of the curves labelled 1–4 could have been produced by each of the following reactions?

(i) Adding excess calcium carbonate to 100 cm³ of 0.05 M hydrochloric acid.

(ii) Adding excess calcium carbonate to 50 cm³ of 0.2 M hydrochloric acid.   (2 marks)

Total: 30 marks

■ ■ ■

Grade-A answer to Question 2

(a) (i)

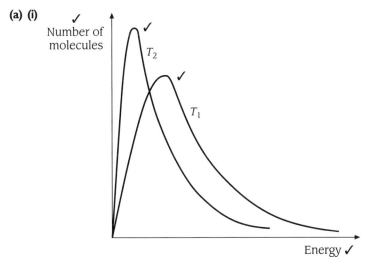

e There is 1 mark for each correctly labelled axis, leaving only 2 marks for the two curves. Curve T_1 must start at the origin and not touch the x-axis. Curve T_2 is at a lower temperature, so it must be to the left of T_1 and the peak of T_2 must be higher than that of T_1.

(ii) There would be no change in the presence of a catalyst ✓.

A larger mass of gas would result in a higher curve, because there are more molecules in the sample ✓. The curve would show the same distribution of energies and the peak would be at the same point, because the molecules have the same distribution of energies — there are just more of them ✓.

e Only temperature alters the distribution of molecular energies. A larger mass gives a larger surface area under the curve, but the distribution is still the same.

(b) Increase the concentration of the solution ✓. There will be more particles ✓, leading to a greater collision frequency ✓.

Decrease the particle size of the solid (use a powdered solid) ✓. This increases the surface area ✓, leading to a greater collision frequency ✓.

Increase the temperature ✓. This increases the average energy of the particles ✓, so more particles will have energy greater than the energy of activation ✓.

e Keep your answer concise. There are 9 marks for the three different ways of increasing the rate, i.e. 3 marks per method. 1 mark is for stating the method used and 2 marks are for the explanation, which must refer to collision theory.

(c) (i) Determine the gradient ✓ of the tangent to the curve at time = 0 ✓ (or at point A).

(ii) The initial rate is greatest at point A ✓ because there are more particles and this gives the greatest collision frequency ✓. The rate decreases at point B ✓ because there are fewer particles, so there is a lower collision frequency ✓. The rate approaches zero at point C ✓ because no particles remain, so the reaction is complete ✓.

(iii) The curve would be steeper ✓ because the rate of reaction increases with temperature ✓.

The curve would end at the same point ✓ because the same amount of acid has been used, resulting in the same loss in mass ✓.

e You need to be able to interpret practical results and explain them in terms of collision theory. In part (iii), a correct sketch would score 2 marks but an explanation is needed for the other 2 marks.

(d) (i) 4 ✓

e Curve 4 is correct because half the number of moles of HCl have been used, so only half the amount of CO_2 is evolved. The initial rate is lower, because fewer particles are present in the same volume of solution.

(ii) 1 ✓

e Curve 1 is correct because the same number of moles of HCl have been used, so the same amount of CO_2 is evolved. The initial rate is higher because the same number of particles is present in a smaller volume. Therefore, there are more particles per unit volume, leading to a greater collision frequency.

Grade-A answer to Question 3

(a) (i) The reaction is endothermic ✓ in the forward direction. An increase in temperature causes an increase in the equilibrium concentration of hydrogen ✓, because the equilibrium position shifts to the right-hand side ✓ to lower the temperature.

(ii) There is an increase in the number of moles in the forward direction ✓. An increase in pressure causes a decrease in the equilibrium concentration of the hydrogen ✓, because the equilibrium position shifts to the left-hand side ✓ to decrease the pressure.

(iii) An increase in the concentration of methane causes an increase in the equilibrium concentration of hydrogen ✓, because the equilibrium position shifts to the right-hand side to remove the added methane ✓.

e When explaining the effect of temperature and pressure on a system at equilibrium, always include three key points for each factor — the effect on the equilibrium position, what happens to oppose the change and the exothermic or endothermic nature (when discussing temperature) or the number of moles on each side (when discussing pressure). Remember that when a product is removed, the system will always move to replace it.

(b) (i) An increase in pressure causes an increase in the product yield ✓. An increase in pressure shifts the equilibrium position to the right-hand side to decrease the pressure ✓. The forward reaction must involve a decrease in the number of moles ✓.

e It is essential that your first statement uses information from the graph.

(ii) A decrease in temperature causes an increase in the yield of the product ✓. A decrease in temperature shifts the equilibrium position to the right-hand side to increase the temperature ✓. The forward reaction must be exothermic ✓.

e It is essential that your first statement uses information from the graph.

(iii) 70% ✓

e The sketch graph in part (b) means that the values accepted will range from 65% to 75%.

(iv) A very low temperature would produce a very low reaction rate ✓. A very high pressure would increase the costs of building the plant and high pressure is expensive to maintain ✓.

e The choice of temperature for an exothermic reaction involves a compromise between a high yield and a low rate. If the temperature is too low, the rate becomes unacceptably low. High pressures encourage both a high yield and a high rate, but cost becomes a problem.

Equilibria

(3) The equation below describes the steam reforming of methane:

$$CH_4(g) + H_2O(g) \longrightarrow 3H_2(g) + CO(g)$$

The enthalpy change for the formation of carbon monoxide and hydrogen is +210 kJ mol^{-1}.

(a) State and explain the effect on the equilibrium concentration of hydrogen of:

    (i) an increase in temperature

    (ii) an increase in total pressure

    (iii) an increase methane concentration   **(8 marks)**

(b) The equilibrium yield of a product in a gas-phase reaction varies with changes in temperature and pressure, as shown below.

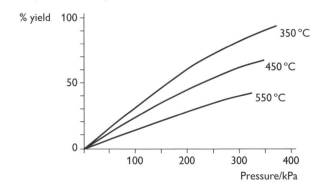

    (i) Use the information given above to deduce whether the forward reaction involves an increase in, a decrease in or no change in the number of moles present. Explain your answer.   **(3 marks)**

    (ii) Use the information given above to deduce whether the forward reaction is exothermic or endothermic. Explain your answer.   **(3 marks)**

    (iii) Estimate the percentage yield of product that would be obtained at 350 °C and a pressure of 250 kPa.   **(1 mark)**

    (iv) The highest yields in this reaction are obtained at very low temperature and very high pressure. Explain why the industrial process avoids the use of very low temperature and very high pressure.   **(2 marks)**

(c) Octane (C_8H_{18}) can be produced from carbon monoxide and hydrogen in the presence of an iron and cobalt catalyst:

$$8CO(g) + 17H_2(g) \longrightarrow C_8H_{18}(g) + 8H_2O(g)$$

    (i) Use the following data to estimate the enthalpy change for the reaction.

Substance	$H_2O(g)$	$CO(g)$	$C_8H_{18}(g)$
Enthalpy of formation/kJ mol^{-1}	−242	−111	−169

                                                 (4 marks)

    (ii) Predict and explain the optimum industrial conditions for the production of octane.   **(9 marks)**

                                                Total: 30 marks

(c) (i) $\Delta H_r = \Sigma \Delta H_f$ products $- \Sigma \Delta H_f$ reactants ✓

$= -169 + 8(-242) - 8(-111)$ ✓ ✓

$= -1217\,kJ\,mol^{-1}$ ✓

There is 1 mark for either a cycle or the statement $\Delta H_r = \Sigma \Delta H_f$ products $- \Sigma \Delta H_f$ reactants. 2 marks are for multiplying -242 by 8 and multiplying -111 by 8, while the answer, -1217, scores the final mark.

(ii) The reaction is exothermic ✓ in the forward direction, so a low temperature favours a high yield ✓. However, a low temperature would produce a low rate ✓ of reaction. A moderate temperature ✓ would be employed as a compromise. The reaction involves a decrease in the number of moles ✓ in the forward direction, so a high pressure favours a high yield ✓. A high pressure also produces a high rate ✓ of reaction. However, high pressure is expensive to produce and maintain ✓. A moderate pressure would be employed as a compromise between yield/rate and cost ✓.

A catalyst is used to lower the energy of activation ✓ and increase the rate of reaction ✓. The catalyst has no effect on the yield ✓.

There are 12 marks shown in the answer, but a maximum of 9 marks can be awarded — this is quite common for questions of this type. Do not be intimidated when faced with unfamiliar reactions. This reaction involves a decrease in the number of moles, it is exothermic and it uses a catalyst, so the arguments are the same as those for the Haber process. If the answer to (c) (i) is incorrect but still exothermic, there is no change to the marking scheme for part (c) (ii). However, if the answer is incorrect and endothermic, you are still given credit in part (c) (ii) for discussing your answer in terms of an endothermic reaction.

Redox reactions

(4) (a) Deduce the oxidation states of chlorine in the following species:
- HCl
- NaClO
- ClF_3
- $KClO_4$
- Cl_2O_7
- ClO_3^- (6 marks)

(b) Which of the following reactions, involving chlorine compounds, are examples of redox reactions?

(i) $2NH_3 + 3Cl_2 \longrightarrow N_2 + 6HCl$

(ii) $2HCl + Ba(OH)_2 \longrightarrow BaCl_2 + 2H_2O$

(iii) $MnO_2 + 4HCl \longrightarrow MnCl_2 + Cl_2 + 2H_2O$

(iv) $NaClO + 2HI \longrightarrow NaCl + H_2O + I_2$

If the reaction is not a redox reaction, then indicate this by stating 'not redox'. In the redox reactions, state whether the chlorine species has been oxidised or reduced during the reaction. (7 marks)

(c) For each equation below, identify the element that has been reduced and state the oxidation state of this element before and after the reaction.

(i) $2HI + H_2SO_4 \longrightarrow I_2 + SO_2 + 2H_2O$ (3 marks)

(ii) $Cu + 4HNO_3 \longrightarrow Cu(NO_3)_2 + 2NO_2 + 2H_2O$ (3 marks)

(iii) $KIO_3 + 2Na_2SO_3 \longrightarrow KIO + 2Na_2SO_4$ (3 marks)

(d) Deduce the half-equations for:

(i) the reduction of a chlorate(I) ion, ClO^-, to a chloride ion, Cl^- (1 mark)

(ii) the oxidation of an iodide ion, I^-, to iodine, I_2 (1 mark)

(iii) Use these half-equations to deduce the redox equation for the reaction of a chlorate(I) ion with an iodide ion in acidic conditions. (1 mark)

(e) When chlorine is bubbled into cold, dilute, aqueous sodium hydroxide, the following equilibrium is established:

$Cl_2 + 2OH^- \rightleftharpoons Cl^- + ClO^- + H_2O$

(i) Show that this is a redox reaction by considering the oxidation states of the chlorine-containing species in the equilibrium mixture. (3 marks)

(ii) Identify the oxidising agent in the forward direction of the equilibrium and the reducing agent in the backward direction of the equilibrium. (2 marks)

Total: 30 marks

■ ■ ■

Grade-A answer to Question 4

(a) -1 ✓, $+1$ ✓, $+3$ ✓, $+7$ ✓, $+7$ ✓, $+5$ ✓

e No working out needs to be shown to achieve full marks. The basic principles are: oxygen is oxidation state -2, hydrogen is $+1$ and the alkali metals are $+1$. The sum of the oxidation states in a compound is zero and the sum of the oxidation states in an ion is equal to the overall charge on the ion.

(b) (i) Redox ✓; chlorine is reduced ✓.

e The oxidation states are 0 and -1.

(ii) Not redox ✓

e The oxidation states are -1 and -1.

(iii) Redox ✓; chlorine is oxidised ✓.

e The oxidation states are -1 and 0. $MnCl_2$ contains two Cl^- ions and therefore some of the Cl^- ions are not oxidised in this redox reaction.

(iv) Redox ✓; chlorine is reduced ✓.

e The oxidation states are $+1$ and -1.

✐ No explanations are required to achieve full marks. If the oxidation state of an element decreases, then it has been reduced. If the oxidation state increases, then it has been oxidised.

(c) (i) Sulphur ✓; +6 ✓; +4 ✓
   (ii) Nitrogen ✓; +5 ✓; +4 ✓
   (iii) Iodine ✓; +5 ✓; +1 ✓

✐ Full marks can only be awarded if the changes in the oxidation states are related to the correct element.

(d) (i) $ClO^- + 2H^+ + 2e^- \longrightarrow Cl^- + H_2O$ ✓
   (ii) $2I^- \longrightarrow I_2 + 2e^-$ ✓
   (iii) $ClO^- + 2H^+ + 2I^- \longrightarrow Cl^- + H_2O + I_2$ ✓

✐ This is a straightforward question. The half-equations are balanced using H_2O, H^+ and e^- where appropriate. Combining the two half-equations cancels out $2e^-$ to produce an overall redox equation.

(e) (i) $Cl_2 + 2OH^- \rightleftharpoons Cl^- + ClO^- + H_2O$
   The oxidation state of chlorine in Cl_2 is 0 ✓.
   In Cl^- it is –1 ✓.
   In ClO^- it is +1 ✓.

✐ An oxidising agent is reduced during the reaction — its oxidation state decreases, i.e. Cl_2 (0) $\longrightarrow Cl^-$ (–1). A reducing agent is oxidised during the reaction and it increases its oxidation state, i.e. Cl (–1) $\longrightarrow Cl_2$ (0).

   (ii) The oxidising agent in the forward direction is Cl_2 ✓ and the reducing agent in the backward direction is Cl^- ✓.

✐ Cl_2 is also acting as a reducing agent in the forward direction, because it is also oxidised, i.e. Cl_2 (0) $\longrightarrow ClO^-$ (+1). The simultaneous oxidation and reduction of chlorine in the forward direction is an example of disproportionation.

Group 7: the halogens

(5) When concentrated sulphuric acid, H_2SO_4, is added to solid sodium iodide, hydrogen iodide is evolved. In further reactions, the hydrogen iodide is converted to iodine and the sulphuric acid is converted to a mixture of products, one of which is hydrogen sulphide (H_2S).
   (a) (i) Write an equation for the formation of hydrogen iodide from sodium iodide and concentrated sulphuric acid and state the role of the concentrated sulphuric acid in the reaction. (2 marks)
   (ii) Deduce the oxidation states of sulphur in H_2SO_4 and H_2S. (2 marks)

(iii) **Write half-equations for the conversion of:**
- iodide ions to iodine   (1 mark)
- sulphuric acid to hydrogen sulphide   (1 mark)

   (iv) **Use the half-equations in (iii) to deduce the overall equation for this reaction.**   (1 mark)

   (v) **State the role of sulphuric acid in the conversion of iodide ions into iodine.**   (1 mark)

   (vi) **State two other possible products that could be obtained from sulphuric acid during the reaction with hydrogen iodide.**   (2 marks)

   (vii) **Identify a solid sodium halide which, when reacted with concentrated sulphuric acid, does not reduce it.**   (1 mark)

   (viii) **Identify a solid sodium halide that reduces concentrated sulphuric acid to sulphur dioxide.**   (1 mark)

(b) Iodine is liberated quantitatively when household bleach is treated with potassium iodide in acid solution. The active ingredient in the bleach is sodium chlorate(I) and it is the chlorate(I) ion which oxidises the iodide ions to iodine. 10.0 cm^3 of bleach were made up to 250 cm^3 of solution with distilled water. Then, 25.0 cm^3 of this dilute solution were treated with an excess of potassium iodide and acidified with sulphuric acid. The liberated iodine required 15.4 cm^3 of 0.100 M sodium thiosulphate.

   (i) **Write separate equations for the reaction of:**
- the chlorate(I) ion with iodide ions in the presence of acid (H$^+$ ions)   (2 marks)
- the reaction of iodine with thiosulphate ions   (2 marks)

   (ii) **Name a suitable indicator to detect the end-point for the titration of iodine with sodium thiosulphate and describe the colour change at the end-point when this indicator is used.**   (3 marks)

   (iii) **Use the information above to calculate the concentration, in g dm^{-3}, of sodium chlorate(I) in household bleach.**   (11 marks)

                                    Total: 30 marks

■ ■ ■

Grade-A answer to Question 5

(a) (i) $NaI + H_2SO_4 \longrightarrow NaHSO_4 + HI$ ✓

      H_2SO_4 is acting as a strong acid ✓ by donating a proton, H$^+$.

e An alternative equation is $2NaI + H_2SO_4 \longrightarrow Na_2SO_4 + 2HI$; a proton donor is an alternative answer to a strong acid.

(ii) +6 in H_2SO_4 ✓; −2 in H_2S ✓

e No explanations are required.

(iii) $2I^- \longrightarrow I_2 + 2e^-$ ✓

      $H_2SO_4 + 8H^+ + 8e^- \longrightarrow H_2S + 4H_2O$ ✓

e An alternative half-equation is $SO_4^{2-} + 10H^+ + 8e^- \longrightarrow H_2S + 4H_2O$

(iv) $H_2SO_4 + 8HI \longrightarrow H_2S + 4H_2O + 4I_2$ ✓

e An alternative overall equation is $SO_4^{2-} + 10H^+ + 8I^- \longrightarrow H_2S + 4H_2O + 4I_2$

(v) H_2SO_4 is acting as an oxidising agent ✓.

e An oxidising agent accepts electrons; its oxidation state is decreased.

(vi) Sulphur dioxide ✓ and sulphur ✓.

e H_2SO_4 is reduced to SO_2, S and H_2S.

(vii) NaCl ✓

e NaF is an alternative answer.

(viii) NaBr ✓

e NaAt is an alternative answer.

(b) (i) $ClO^- + 2H^+ + 2I^- \longrightarrow Cl^- + H_2O + I_2$ ✓ ✓
      $I_2 + 2S_2O_3^{2-} \longrightarrow 2I^- + S_4O_6^{2-}$ ✓ ✓

e It is essential that you can recall these two equations as required by the AQA specification. The calculation in part (iii) depends on your ability to write out these equations.

(ii) Starch ✓ indicator changes from blue-black ✓ to colourless ✓ at the end-point.

e These are three straightforward marks, provided that you have revised this section thoroughly.

(iii) Moles of thiosulphate used = $MV/1000 = 0.1 \times 15.4/1000 = 1.54 \times 10^{-3}$ ✓
      Moles of iodine = $\frac{1}{2}(1.54 \times 10^{-3})$ ✓ $= 7.7 \times 10^{-4}$ ✓
      Moles of ClO^- in $25\,cm^3 = 7.7 \times 10^{-4}$ ✓
      Moles of ClO^- in $250\,cm^3 = 7.7 \times 10^{-3}$ ✓
      Moles of ClO^- in $10\,cm^3$ of undiluted bleach $= 7.7 \times 10^{-3}$ ✓
      Moles of ClO^- in $1\,dm^3$ of undiluted bleach $= 7.7 \times 10^{-1}$ ✓
      M_r of NaClO $= 23 + 35.5 + 16 = 74.5$ ✓
      Mass of NaClO in $1\,dm^3$ of undiluted bleach $= 74.5 \times 7.7 \times 10^{-1}$ ✓
      Mass of NaClO per $dm^3 = 57.365$ ✓ $= 57.4\,g\,dm^{-3}$ ✓ (3 significant figures)

e The correct answer expressed to the appropriate number of significant figures scores 11 marks. A common mistake is not dividing the moles of thiosulphate used by 2. This leads to a final answer of 114.7, which would be awarded 9 marks. In order to work out your mark for this section, mark each stage separately. If you have made a mistake in one section, carry on marking the rest of the calculation. You can score marks in the remaining sections, provided that the method is correct.

Extraction of metals

(6) (a) Iron is extracted from the ore haematite, which occurs abundantly in the Earth's crust.

   (i) State the raw materials that are used in the extraction of iron from haematite. (2 marks)

   (ii) Carbon monoxide is used to convert iron(III) oxide into iron. Write two equations to show how carbon is converted to carbon dioxide, which then reacts with carbon to produce carbon monoxide. (2 marks)

   (iii) Write an equation for the reaction of iron(III) oxide with carbon monoxide. Use oxidation states to explain why this is an example of a redox reaction and state the role of carbon monoxide in this reaction. (6 marks)

   (iv) State the principal impurity present in iron produced in a blast furnace and briefly explain the essential chemistry of the process in decreasing the proportion of this impurity. (3 marks)

   (v) State one other impurity present in the iron and explain how it is removed during the conversion to steel. (3 marks)

   (b) (i) Explain why carbon reduction cannot be used in the extraction of aluminium and titanium. (3 marks)

   (ii) Explain why aluminium is more expensive to extract than iron. (2 marks)

   (iii) Describe briefly how titanium is extracted, starting from TiO_2. (5 marks)

   (iv) Explain why titanium metal is expensive to produce. (2 marks)

   (v) Give two properties of titanium that make it useful, despite its cost. (2 marks)

Total: 30 marks

■ ■ ■

Grade-A answer to Question 6

(a) (i) Limestone ✓ and coke ✓

e Haematite is the other raw material, but this information is given in the question.

   (ii) $C + O_2 \longrightarrow CO_2$ ✓
   $CO_2 + C \longrightarrow 2CO$ ✓

e State symbols are not essential.

   (iii) $Fe_2O_3 + 3CO \longrightarrow 2Fe + 3CO_2$ ✓
   Iron is reduced, because its oxidation state changes from +3 ✓ to 0 ✓.
   Carbon is oxidised, because its oxidation state changes from +2 ✓ to +4 ✓.
   Carbon monoxide is acting as a reducing agent ✓.

e You must relate the changes in oxidation state to the element in the equation.

   (iv) The principal impurity is carbon ✓. It is removed by blasting oxygen through ✓, which removes carbon as gaseous carbon monoxide ✓ or carbon dioxide.

e Do not give too much detail in the answers. The examiner is looking for three key points: carbon, blast through of oxygen and carbon monoxide removal.

(v) Sulphur ✓ is another impurity. It is removed by reacting with magnesium ✓ to produce magnesium sulphide ✓.

e Other impurities include phosphorus and silicon. These are oxidised by blasting through oxygen. The addition of calcium oxide (lime) to these oxides forms slag, which is removed.

(b) (i) Aluminium cannot be extracted using carbon, because the temperatures required are too high ✓.
Titanium cannot be extracted using carbon, because titanium reacts with carbon to produce titanium carbide ✓, which makes the metal very brittle ✓.

e The limitations of carbon reduction are stated in the AQA specification, so you must be able to explain them.

(ii) Aluminium requires vast quantities of electricity ✓, and the graphite electrodes must be regularly replaced ✓.

e The need for the addition of cryolite is another possible answer.

(iii) Stage 1: $TiO_2 + 2C + 2Cl_2 \longrightarrow TiCl_4 + 2CO$ ✓✓ (temperature is 900 °C ✓)
Stage 2: $TiCl_4 + 4Na \longrightarrow Ti + 4NaCl$ ✓✓ (temperature is 550–1000 °C ✓)
Stage 2 is carried out in an inert atmosphere of argon ✓.

e Two fully balanced equations score 4 marks. If no equations are given, marks can be awarded for the raw materials in stage 1 (carbon and chlorine) and for the reductant in stage 2 (sodium or magnesium). It is important that the conditions are included.

(iv) Titanium is expensive to produce. This is because it is produced by a batch process ✓, it uses expensive raw materials (i.e. sodium and chlorine) ✓ and special precautions need to be taken with the intermediate, $TiCl_4$, because it reacts violently with water ✓. Also, in stage 2, an expensive argon atmosphere ✓ is used to prevent oxidation of the titanium.

e In this grade-A answer, four reasons have been given. Only two of these are needed for 2 marks.

(v) Titanium has a low density ✓ and it is resistant to corrosion ✓.

e Titanium is strong is another possible answer.